GRAMMAR RULES!

Second edition

Tanya Gibb

STUDENT BOOK 3

Grammar in the real world

Name: _____

Class: _____

Note to Teachers and Parents

Grammar Rules!

Grammar Rules! comprehensively meets the requirements of the Australian Curriculum English. The scope and sequence outlined on pages 4–5 integrates Language, Literature and Literacy to develop students' knowledge, understanding and skills in listening, reading, viewing, speaking and representing.

Grammar Rules! also supports the New Zealand English Curriculum strands: Listening, Reading and Viewing; and Speaking, Writing and Presenting. Students will use processes and strategies to develop knowledge, skills and understandings, related to purposes and audiences, ideas, language features and structure.

Grammar can be defined as the way language is organised to make meaning. Knowledge of the grammatical features that make language use more effective is vital for all students. They need an understanding of grammar to be able to make appropriate choices to get their message across in speaking and writing (creating texts); and they need to know how to analyse the language used by others when they are listening and reading (interpreting texts). Grammatical knowledge will assist students to become analytical, critical and evaluative language users.

Grammar Rules! shows students how grammatical structures and features function in texts to achieve meaning, from the contextual level of the whole text down to sentence level and to the level of words and word parts. The series explains appropriate grammatical structures for particular types of texts, language functions and social purposes. The second edition of the *Grammar Rules!* program also incorporates elements of self-assessment. A simple reflection activity allows students to assess their own progress and provides you with a starting point for discussion.

Student Book 3

Units of work

Student Book 3 contains 35 weekly units of work presented in a conceptually sound scope and sequence. The intention is for students to work through the units in the sequence in which they are presented. See the **Scope and Sequence Chart** on pages 4–5 for more information. There are also regular Revision Units that can be used for consolidation or assessment purposes.

The sample texts in *Student Book 3* are based around the theme of discoveries and inventions. The subject matter of the sample texts is not tied to any particular content across other curriculum areas. This allows teachers and students to focus on the way language is structured according to purpose and audience. Students can then use this knowledge to evaluate, respond to and create texts in other learning areas. The concepts in the sample texts link well with the Cross-Curriculum Priority of Sustainability, as well the General Capabilities of Critical and Creative Thinking, Personal and Social Capability, Ethical Understanding and Intercultural Understanding, as described in the Australian Curriculum.

Icons

 Encourages students to create texts of their own to demonstrate their understanding of the grammatical concepts taught in the unit. These activities focus on written language; however, many also provide opportunities for using spoken language to engage with others, make presentations and develop skills in using ICT.

 Highlights useful grammatical rules and concepts. The rule is always introduced the first time students need it to complete an activity.

 Tells students that a special hint is provided for an activity. It might be a tip about language functions, or a reminder to look at a rule in a previous unit.

 Allows students to assess their progress through each unit.

Grammar Rules Glossary

A valuable glossary is provided at the end of *Student Book 3*. Teachers and students can use this as a straightforward dictionary of grammar terminology, or as a summary of important grammar rules used in *Student Book 3*. Page references are also given for the point in the book where the rule was first introduced, so that students can go back to that unit if they need more information or further revision of the rule.

PULL-OUT WRITING LOG

At the centre of *Student Book 3* is a practical pull-out Writing Log so that students can directly relate the grammar they learn back to their own writing. Students could store the Writing Log in their writing folders, and use it to keep track of the grammar, language functions and types of texts they use. The Writing Log also includes a handy reminder of the writing process, as well as a checklist of types of texts and text forms for students to try.

UNIT AT A GLANCE

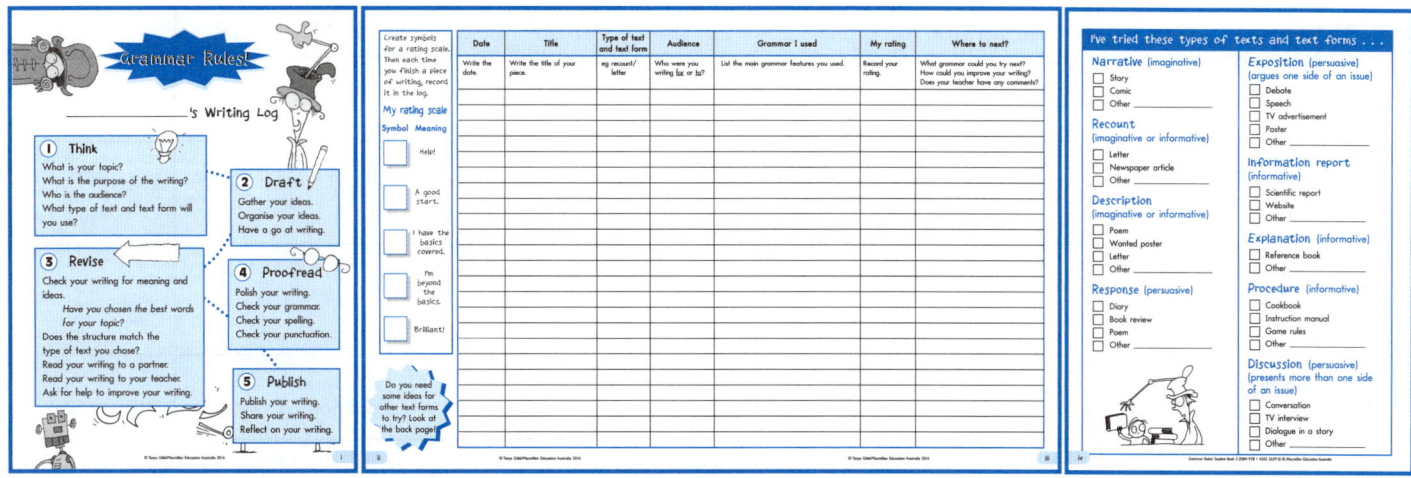

Unit tag — States the main grammar focus

Text sample — Illustrates the grammar focus at work, in the real context of a specific type of text

Sequenced activities — Each activity focuses on a specific aspect of grammar

Tip! — Reminds or gives a special hint

Type of text — Highlights the type of text and purpose of the sample text, and any particular grammar focus

Rule! — Introduces students to a new concept

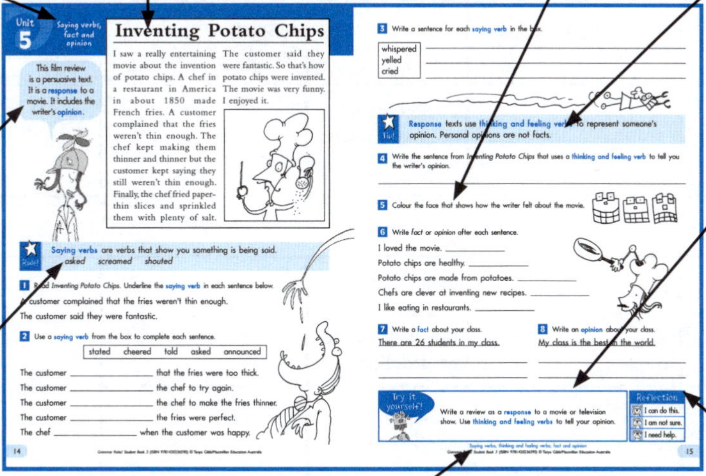

Try it yourself! — Gives students the opportunity to apply grammar in the context of their own texts using the sample texts as models. Provides opportunities for planning, drafting and editing texts using software and word processing programs to publish them

Reflection — Allows students to assess their progress

Footer — Lists the full grammar focus covered in the unit

Grammar Rules! Teacher Resource Book 3–6

Full teacher support for *Student Book 3* is provided by *Grammar Rules! Teacher Resource Book 3–6*. Here you will find valuable background information about grammar, along with practical resources, such as:

- ☆ strategies for teaching grammar
- ☆ grammar games and activities
- ☆ assessment strategies
- ☆ teaching tips for every unit in *Student Book 3*
- ☆ answers for every unit in *Student Book 3*

3

SCOPE AND SEQUENCE

This scope and sequence chart is based on the requirements of the Australian Curriculum.

Unit	Unit name/Type of text	Clause to whole text level			Word and word group level		
		Sentences and clauses	Cohesion: theme, pronouns, lexical chains, connectives	Mood and modality, language and vocabulary	Nouns and noun groups	Verbs and verb groups	Adverbs and prepositional phrases
1	Museum Visit — Recount				proper and common nouns	doing verbs; past tense	
2	A Tasty Invention — Recount	sentences			proper and common nouns	thinking and feeling verbs	
3	Dear Nana and Pop — Response/Email	simple sentences; clauses	1st and 2nd person personal pronouns: I, me, we, us, you			thinking and feeling verbs	
4	The Case of the Missing Robots — Narrative		personal pronouns: she, he, him, her, they, them, it		noun groups with adjectives		
5	Inventing Potato Chips — Response/Film review			fact and opinion		saying verbs; thinking and feeling verbs	
6	REVISION						
7	My Special Place — Narrative/Poem	phrases			noun groups with adjectives		prepositional phrases
8	Nintendo — Information report		personal pronouns	technical words	proper nouns	relating verbs	
9	Penicillin — Recount			questions and statements			time words and phrases
10	Molly's Discovery — Narrative		conjunctions (connectives)		singular and plural nouns	subject/verb agreement	
11	Search for the Lost Valley — Narrative			exclamations; onomatopoeia			adverbs to tell how
12	REVISION						
13	Trampolines — Discussion/Conversation	quoted speech; speech marks		evaluative words; apostrophes for contractions		saying verbs	
14	The Thing Inside — Narrative			modality; emotive words			
15	Where to Find the Hidden Treasure — Procedure/Directions			commands		doing verbs	prepositional phrases and adverbs
16	Wiz Bang 3000 Kitchen Hand! — Advertisement		personal pronouns	emotive words; modality (modal verbs, modal adverbs)			
17	Discovery: A New Species — Description				noun groups; articles; comparing adjectives		
18	REVISION						

Unit	Unit name/ Type of text	Clause to whole text level			Word and word group level		
		Sentences and clauses	Cohesion: theme, pronouns, lexical chains, connectives	Mood and modality, language and vocabulary	Nouns and noun groups	Verbs and verb groups	Adverbs and prepositional phrases
19	Voyagers Description/Poem			simile; idiom	apostrophes for possession		
20	Everyone Should Recycle Exposition/Speech		connectives	fact and opinion			
21	Professor Snodgrass Fails Again Narrative/Comic strip	quoted speech		stereotypes			
22	Dinosaur Found at Local School Recount/Newspaper article	reported speech		emotive words; sensationalism	concrete and abstract nouns		
23	The Jacket Narrative			time words		past, present and future tense	adverbs and prepositions
24	REVISION						
25	The Best New Invention Discussion		connectives	modality	noun groups		
26	Breakfast Inventions Description/Poem		lexical chains	metaphor	descriptive adjectives		
27	Wart, Fester and Carbuncle Remover Procedure/Recipe			commands	number adjectives (quantifiers)	doing verbs	adverbs to tell how
28	How Does the Alarm Bed Work? Explanation		connectives	technical language; evaluative language	nouns	doing verbs	
29	How to Use the Drolley (or Dog Trolley) Procedure/Instructions			evaluative language	noun groups; classifying adjectives		
30	REVISION						
31	My Home Narrative/Poem		personal pronouns	evaluative language	collective nouns		
32	Trying to Negotiate Discussion/Conversation	quoted speech	synonyms	statements; questions; commands; exclamations			
33	Dear Diary Response/Diary	quoted speech; speech marks	lexical chains; synonyms	evaluative language			
34	The Invention of Money Information report	commas in noun lists	personal pronouns	homophones	noun groups; commas in noun lists		
35	REVISION						

5

Unit 1

Nouns, doing verbs

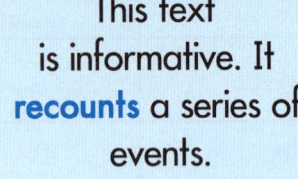

This text is informative. It *recounts* a series of events.

Museum Visit

Last weekend my mum took me to the National Museum of Australia in Canberra. We left home at 7 am and drove for two hours. We arrived before the museum even opened. I was excited to be able to go inside when it opened at 10 am. I saw lots of interesting exhibits and displays. There was also a special area for kids. We ate sandwiches and milkshakes for lunch in the Museum Café. After lunch we went for a walk beside Lake Burley Griffin. The museum closed at five o'clock so we finally had to go home.

★ Rule!

Nouns are words for people, places, animals or things.
Proper nouns are the names of particular people, places, animals or things. They begin with a capital letter.
  Saturday   Stephen   Tasmanian devil   December   Hobart
Common nouns are everyday naming words.
  day   scientist   dinosaur   month   car

1 Read *Museum Visit*. Write the **common nouns** used.

people _____

places _____

food _____

2 Write the **proper nouns** used in *Museum Visit*.

_____

_____

3 Underline six **nouns** for people, places, animals or things.

We parked our car under a tree.
We watched a film about bees.
We sat at a table to eat.
Many people visit the museum.

4 Circle the **noun** in each row.

dog	skipped	ate	played
visited	drove	saw	cat
stopped	bird	climbed	watched
jumped	tickled	swan	said
talked	sang	wiggled	wombat

Rule! **Doing verbs** tell the actions that are happening. Sometimes the way a verb is written lets you know that the action happened in the past. This is called **past tense**.

jumped   ran   made   wrote

5 Underline a **doing verb** in each sentence.

We ate lunch.
Mum drove the car.
Dad worked on his invention.
I built a robot.
We played catch.

6 Write the **past tense** form for each **doing verb**. Hint! You'll find the answers in *Museum Visit*.

drive _____
take _____
see _____
eat _____
close _____

7 Choose a **doing verb** from the box to complete each sentence.

| visited   worked   slept   swam |

We _____ the museum.
Ducks _____ on the lake.
I _____ well after my big day.
Dad _____ all day.

Try it yourself! Write a **recount** about something that happened to you last weekend. Use **nouns** for people, places and things. Remember to use the **past tense** forms of the verbs.

Reflection
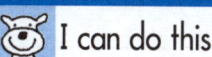 I can do this.
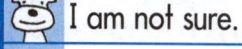 I am not sure.
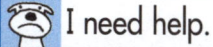 I need help.

Unit 2

Nouns, thinking and feeling verbs

A Tasty Invention

John Montagu invented the first sandwich in 1762. Montagu loved playing card games. He hated to stop playing to eat or even to sleep. One day he was playing a card game that had already lasted 24 hours. He was really hungry so he asked for some slices of bread and some meat. Other card players watched him put the meat in between two slices of bread. He ate with one hand while he continued to play cards with the other. His friends named the bread and meat invention a sandwich because Montagu was the Earl of Sandwich.

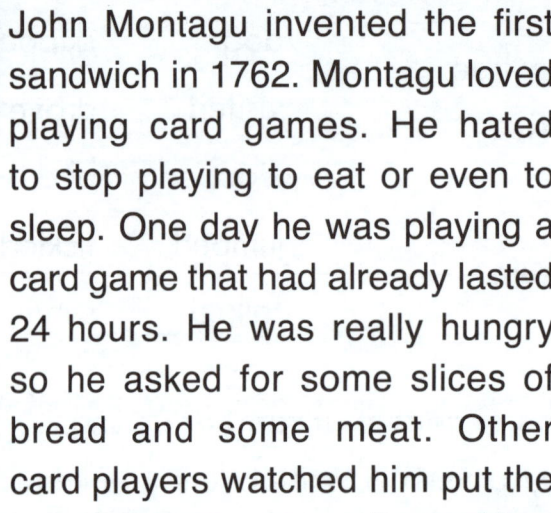

This text is informative. It **recounts** events in a time sequence. It uses **thinking and feeling verbs**.

1 Read *A Tasty Invention*. Circle the **common nouns**.

2 Underline the **proper nouns** used in *A Tasty Invention*.

Tip! Remember the rule on page 6.

Tip! **Sentences** start with a capital letter and end in a full stop, question mark or exclamation mark.

3 Rewrite each sentence with correct punctuation.
Hint! Names for months and days of the week are **proper nouns**.

The Earl of Sandwich is making toast.

john montagu lived in england

_____

the earl of sandwich was very rich

_____

uncle jack lives on woodland road

_____

today is friday

_____

my friends are jin and waiyin

_____

4 Write **common nouns** for things you can

eat _____ _____ _____

play with _____ _____ _____

draw with _____ _____ _____

cuddle _____ _____ _____

Rule! **Thinking and feeling verbs** represent mental activities such as loving, hoping and believing. You can't see these activities taking place.
think   wish   like   consider

5 Write the **thinking and feeling verbs** used in *A Tasty Invention*.

_____ _____

6 Circle the **thinking and feeling verbs**.

Montagu liked meat.

He hoped the sandwich would taste good.

Montagu loved sandwiches.

I enjoyed my sandwiches.

7 Use each **thinking and feeling verb** in a sentence.

| wonder | think | believe | wish |

_____

_____

_____

_____

Try it yourself! Ask a family member to recount something you did when you were a baby. Ask how they felt as they watched you. Write the **recount** using **thinking and feeling verbs**. Remember that people's names are **proper nouns**.

Reflection
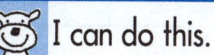 I can do this.
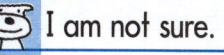 I am not sure.
 I need help.

Unit 3

Clauses, personal pronouns

This email is a **response** that gives the writer's point of view. It uses **personal pronouns**.

Dear Nana and Pop,

I can't wait until the next school holidays so I can visit you. Dad says we can come in two weeks. I am really excited.

Are you excited about seeing us?

Yesterday, Dad told me that archaeologists have discovered cave art in Australia that was painted 170 000 years ago. I think that is incredible. Do you think that is amazing? That means that the Aboriginal people discovered Australia way, way earlier than most people had thought. I miss you! See you soon.

I LOVE YOU, Hannah

Rule!

Personal pronouns replace nouns for people and things.
Some **personal pronouns** refer to the writer or speaker of a text.
   I   me   we   us
Some **personal pronouns** address readers or listeners.
   you

1 Read *Dear Nana and Pop*. Circle the **personal pronouns**.

2 Use each **personal pronoun** in a sentence.

| I | me | we | us | you |

_____

_____

_____

_____

Rule! A **clause** is a group of words that contain a verb. A simple **sentence** is a single clause. A sentence begins with a capital letter and ends with a full stop, question mark or exclamation mark.

3 Tick a column to show whether each group of words is a **sentence**. Hint! Does it make sense? Does it have a **verb**?

Then add a punctuation mark to the end of each group of words that is a **sentence**.

	Sentence	Not a sentence
The finish it hungry dog		
The dog ate my homework		
Nan and Pop		
Dad told me which		
Can Mum cook pancakes		

4 Write a **sentence** to answer each question.

How old are you?

_____

Who lives with you?

_____

What is your favourite food?

_____

5 Underline three **thinking and feeling verbs** in *Dear Nana and Pop*.

6 Circle the **thinking and feeling verbs**.

I like cookies.   I hope I can visit you.

I love banana smoothies.   I think I can jump that high.

Try it yourself! Write a letter to a friend or relative. Tell them about something that you are excited about. Use **thinking and feeling verbs** and **personal pronouns**. Make sure your **sentences** make sense.

Reflection
- I can do this.
- I am not sure.
- I need help.

Simple sentences; clauses; thinking and feeling verbs; 1st and 2nd person personal pronouns: *I, me, we, us, you*

Unit 4: Personal pronouns, adjectives

The Case of the Missing Robots

On a peaceful island just off the coast of Australia there lived a clever inventor. The inventor made robots. The inventor had lived on the island by himself for many years.

He had nobody to talk to, apart from the robots, but he liked it that way. A fast boat arrived each month to collect the finished robots and sell them in Australia.

One day there was a huge explosion outside the robot factory. The inventor went inside to check on his robots but he couldn't find a single one. They had completely disappeared.

This is an imaginative text. It is the beginning of a **narrative**. It uses **noun groups** to describe the characters and set the scene.

Rule! Some **personal pronouns** are used to refer to people being spoken about.
she   he   him   her   they   them
The **personal pronouns** *it*, *they* and *them* can refer to animals, things or places.

1 Read *The Case of the Missing Robots*. Circle the **personal pronouns**.

What **noun** does *he* refer to? _____

What **noun** do *they* and *them* refer to? _____

2 Complete each sentence using a **personal pronoun** from the box.

| he   she   they   them |

_____ went to find his robots.

He couldn't find _____.

_____ were missing.

_____ is a female chimpanzee.

3 Complete each sentence. Use the **personal pronouns** from the box.

| it | it | it | he | them | they |

The island is off the coast. _____ is a beautiful place.
The inventor likes robots. _____ invents _____.
The explosion was outside the factory. _____ was very loud.
A fast boat collects the robots. _____ arrives each month.
The robots had vanished. _____ were nowhere to be seen.

Rule!

A **noun group** is a group of words with a noun. The other words in the noun group tell more about the noun.
  the clever inventor

Adjectives are words in a noun group that describe the noun.
  the clever inventor

---

4 Underline four **adjectives** in *The Case of the Missing Robots*.

5 Form **noun groups**. Add a noun from *The Case of the Missing Robots* to each adjective.

clever _____
peaceful _____
huge _____
fast _____

6 Draw lines to link each **adjective** to a **noun**.

happy   ghost
angry   pirate
scary   smile
ferocious   voice
whiny   frown

7 Write an interesting **adjective** to describe each **noun**.

_____ cat   _____ piglet
_____ gorilla   _____ scientist
_____ boat   _____ baby

Try it yourself! Finish the **narrative** *The Case of the Missing Robots*. Why had the robots disappeared? Use **pronouns** to refer to the robots. Use **adjectives** to describe people, places, animals and things.

Reflection
- I can do this.
- I am not sure.
- I need help.

Noun groups with adjectives; personal pronouns: she, he, him, her, they, them, it

Unit 5: Saying verbs, fact and opinion

Inventing Potato Chips

I saw a really entertaining movie about the invention of potato chips. A chef in a restaurant in America in about 1850 made French fries. A customer complained that the fries weren't thin enough. The chef kept making them thinner and thinner but the customer kept saying they still weren't thin enough. Finally, the chef fried paper-thin slices and sprinkled them with plenty of salt. The customer said they were fantastic. So that's how potato chips were invented. The movie was very funny. I enjoyed it.

This film review is a persuasive text. It is a **response** to a movie. It includes the writer's **opinion**.

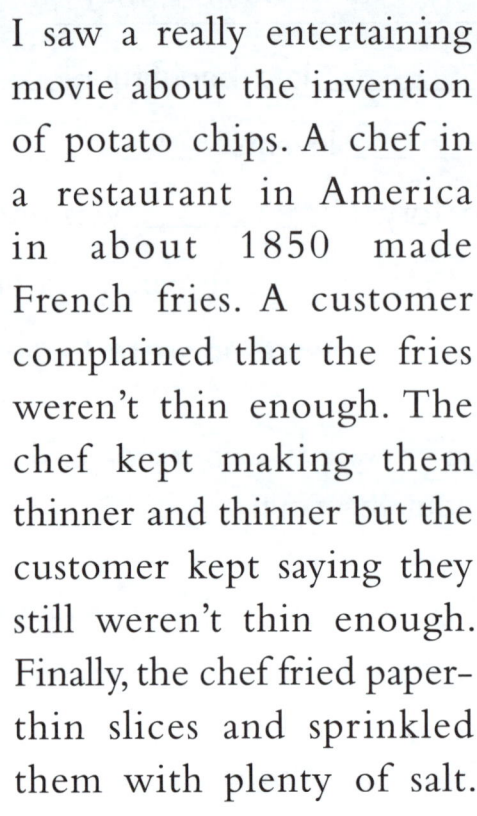

Rule! **Saying verbs** are verbs that show you something is being said.
asked   screamed   shouted

1 Read *Inventing Potato Chips*. Underline the **saying verb** in each sentence below.

A customer complained that the fries weren't thin enough.

The customer said they were fantastic.

2 Use a **saying verb** from the box to complete each sentence.

| stated | cheered | told | asked | announced |

The customer _____ that the fries were too thick.

The customer _____ the chef to try again.

The customer _____ the chef to make the fries thinner.

The customer _____ the fries were perfect.

The chef _____ when the customer was happy.

14

3 Write a sentence for each **saying verb** in the box.

| whispered |
| yelled |
| cried |

_____

_____

_____

> **Tip!** **Response** texts use **thinking and feeling verbs** to represent someone's opinion. Personal opinions are not facts.

4 Write the sentence from _Inventing Potato Chips_ that uses a **thinking and feeling verb** to tell you the writer's opinion.

_____

5 Colour the face that shows how the writer felt about the movie.

6 Write _fact_ or _opinion_ after each sentence.

I loved the movie. _____

Potato chips are healthy. _____

Potato chips are made from potatoes. _____

Chefs are clever at inventing new recipes. _____

I like eating in restaurants. _____

7 Write a **fact** about your class.

<u>There are 26 students in my class.</u>

_____

8 Write an **opinion** about your class.

<u>My class is the best in the world.</u>

_____

Try it yourself! Write a review as a **response** to a movie or television show. Use **thinking and feeling verbs** to tell your opinion.

Reflection
- I can do this.
- I am not sure.
- I need help.

Saying verbs; thinking and feeling verbs; fact and opinion

Unit 6 Revision

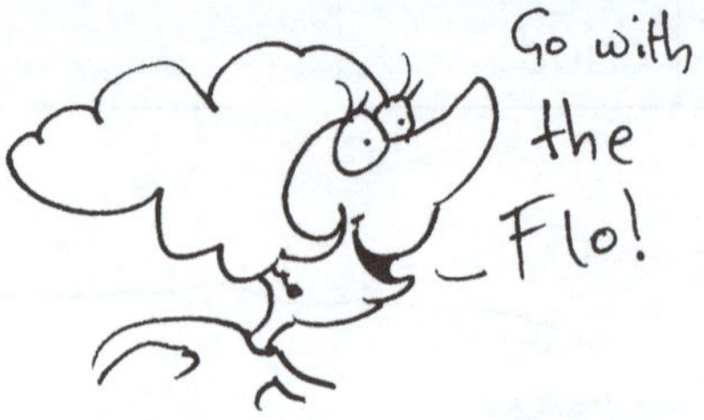

1 Rewrite each sentence with correct punctuation.

aunty flo lives in darwin

____

today is wednesday

____

school holidays start in april

____

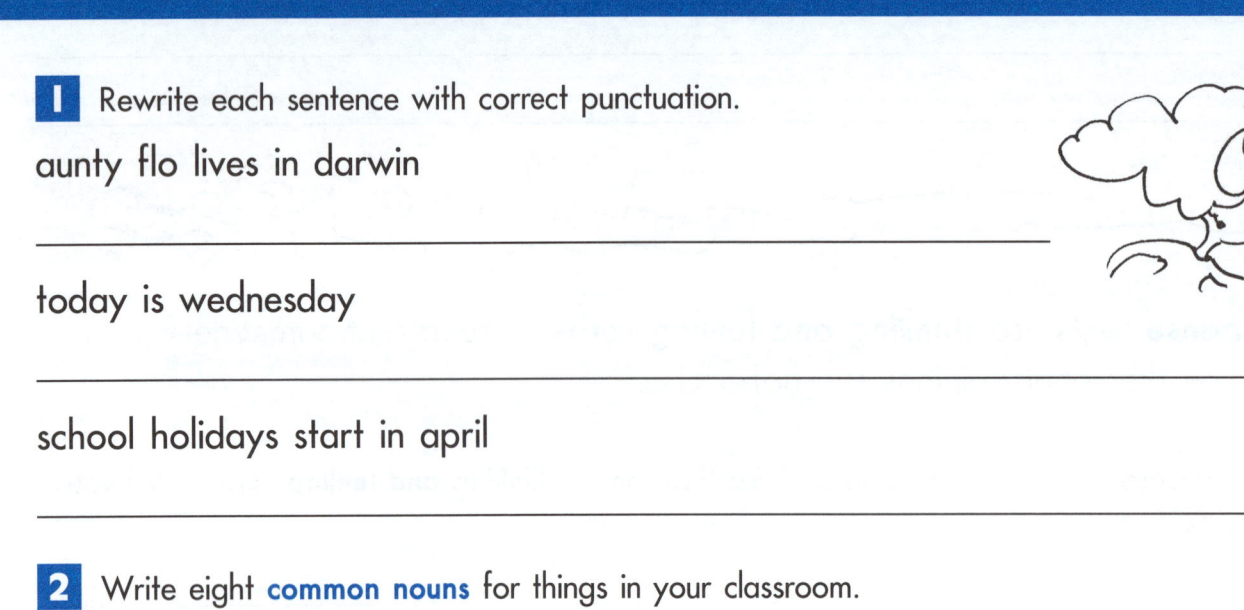

2 Write eight **common nouns** for things in your classroom.

____

____

3 Underline the **doing verbs** in the box.

jumped	house	science	island	invented	cooked

4 Write a sentence to say what each animal did.

____

____

____

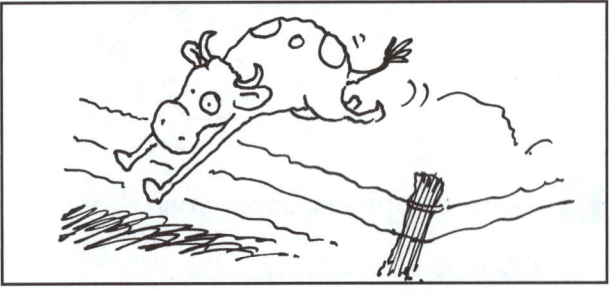

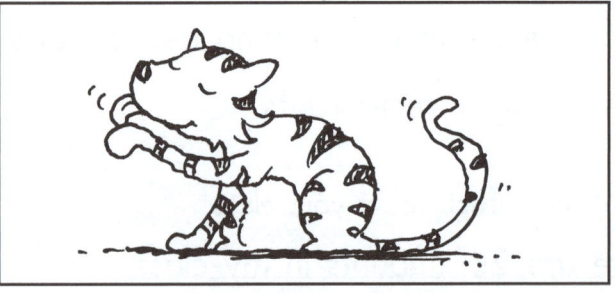

5 Unscramble each **thinking and feeling verb**.

ovedl _______________ tedha _______________ beedliev _______________

pohed _______________ shiwde _______________ eedend _______________

Grammar Rules! Student Book 3 (ISBN 9781420236590) © Tanya Gibb/Macmillan Education Australia

6 Complete each sentence with a **personal pronoun** from the box.

| we | us | they | them |

Give _____ their books.

_____ can come with us.

_____ enjoy watching movies together.

Will you watch the movie with _____?

7 Unjumble the words to make **sentences**. Put a full stop, exclamation mark or question mark at the end. Use a capital letter at the beginning of each sentence.

potato tasty I think chips are

_____

pancakes I love for breakfast to eat

_____

going you the are to watch movie

_____

away go

_____

8 Form **noun groups**. Draw a line to link an **adjective** to each **noun**.

cute	island
sore	king
bossy	dog
old	knee
beautiful	kitten

9 Write *fact* or *opinion* after each sentence.

Computers are machines. _____

All sharks are scary. _____

I love broccoli. _____

Magpies are birds. _____

10 Complete each sentence with a **saying verb**.

The tourist _____ at the bear.

The chef _____ to the customer.

The scientist _____ about her discovery.

The team _____ when they won.

Revision

Unit 7

Prepositions, adjectives

This is an imaginative text in the form of a poem. It uses **adjectives** and **prepositions** for particular effect.

My Special Place

My special place
at the bottom of the yard,
under scraggy bushes,
through prickly hedges,
into a dark tunnel,
beneath the overgrowth –
still and quiet.
Secret place –
discovered and hidden.

Rule! A **preposition** shows the relationship between a **noun** and another word. **Prepositions** can tell <u>where</u>.   in   on   under   over   beside   off   through

1 Read *My Special Place*. Circle the **prepositions**.

2 Complete each sentence with a **preposition** from the box.

| over | under | behind | through | on |

Jump _____ the fence.
Look _____ the rug.
Crawl _____ the tunnel.
Sit _____ the log.
Hide it _____ your back.

3 Circle all the **prepositions** that could be used in this sentence.

I crawled _____ the branch.

| over | through | into | beside |
| from | around | above | along |

4 Circle all the **prepositions** that could be used in this sentence.

I looked _____ the fence.

| during | near | towards | under |
| around | without | before | beyond |

Rule! A **phrase** is a group of words that go together to make meaning. A phrase usually **does not** include a **verb**.
A **prepositional phrase** is a preposition linked to a noun or noun group.
   <u>in</u> the tunnel   <u>under</u> the bushes

5 Create **prepositional phrases**. Write a **noun group** after each preposition.

at _____
under _____
through _____
into _____

Tip! Remember the rule on page 13.

6 Complete each sentence with a **prepositional phrase** to tell <u>where</u>.

The lorikeets chattered _____.
The dog squeezed _____.
The tiger prowled _____.
The worms wriggled _____.

7 Underline the **adjectives** in *My Special Place*.

8 Write new **adjectives** to give a different description of the special place.

under _____ bushes
through _____ hedges
into a _____ tunnel

Tip! Remember the rule on page 13.

9 Write two **adjectives** to describe each **noun**.

_____ _____ apple
_____ _____ bedroom
_____ _____ mango
_____ _____ hamburger

Try it yourself! Write a **poem** about a special place that you have discovered. It could be a cubby house, your local park or somewhere in your home. Use **prepositional phrases** to tell <u>where</u>. Use interesting **adjectives** to describe your special place.

Reflection
- I can do this.
- I am not sure.
- I need help.

Unit 8 — Relating verbs

This informative text is an **information report**. It uses **verbs** that show relationships.

Nintendo

Donkey Kong was the world's first child-friendly video game. It was created in 1981 by inventors at Nintendo. It did not include violence or car chases like all the other video games available back then. Donkey Kong had a storyline based on the fairytale 'Beauty and the Beast'. In 1981, Nintendo was only a small electronics company. It introduced another game, Pac-Man, in 1983. The name Pac-Man comes from a Japanese word 'paku', which means 'eat'. Nintendo is now a hugely successful international company.

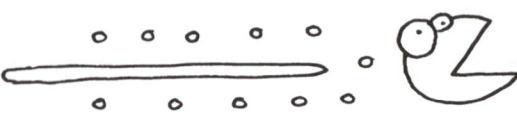

Rule! **Relating verbs** show relationships, such as being and having. You cannot see any action taking place.

is   are   have   has   had   was

1 Read *Nintendo*. Then underline the **relating verb** in each sentence below.

My dad has an old copy of Donkey Kong.

Donkey Kong was the world's first non-violent video game.

It was created in 1981.

Nintendo was a small company.

Donkey Kong had many fans.

Nintendo is a successful company.

2 Choose a **relating verb** to complete each sentence.

| is |
| belong |
| was |
| had |
| are |

My favourite animal _____ a dolphin but now I love whales best.

It _____ time for band practice.

You _____ clever at maths.

The shoes _____ to Nadi.

Irena _____ lunch with her friends.

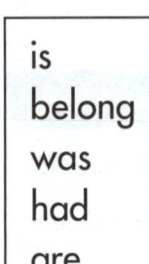

3 What two things does the personal pronoun *it* refer to in *Nintendo*?

_____   _____

4 Complete each sentence with a personal pronoun from the box.

| them |
| she |
| it |
| he |
| they |

_____ are coming to my house after school.

_____ is my brother.

The computer is in my bedroom but _____ is broken.

Some people love video games but I don't enjoy _____ .

Penny broke the plate when _____ was washing the dishes.

5 Cross out the incorrect personal pronoun in each sentence

(They/Them) will collect aluminium cans.

(Him/He) is a great goalkeeper.

(It/She) is a lovely tree.

Give the books to (they/them).

(She/Her) went fishing with Grandpa.

 **Tip!** Information reports often use technical words related to the topic.

6 Circle the technical words in *Nintendo*.

7 Circle the technical words that could be included in an information report about computers.

| monitor | mouse | tomato | busy | program |
| happy | | delete | screen saver | |

8 Write the proper nouns used in *Nintendo*.

_____

_____

Try it yourself! Research a topic of your choice. Write an information report. Use relating verbs and technical words.

Reflection

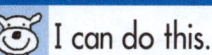 I can do this.

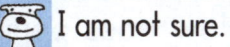 I am not sure.

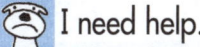 I need help.

Relating verbs: *is, are, have, has, had, was, belong*; personal pronouns; proper nouns; technical words

Unit 9
Questions, statements, time words

This informative text is a **recount**. It uses **time words** to sequence events in history.

PENICILLIN

In 1928, a Scottish scientist named Alexander Fleming was studying bacteria growth. Bacteria are germs that can cause infections in people. Fleming discovered that a mould had grown on one of his dishes and that bacteria could not grow where there was mould. He wrote a report about his discovery. Ten years later Dr Howard Florey, an Australian, discovered the actual substance in the mould that killed the bacteria. Florey and his colleagues had discovered penicillin. Since then, penicillin has saved millions of lives.

Rule!

A **statement** gives information or an opinion. It ends in a full stop.
Alexander Fleming was a scientist.   I think Alexander Fleming was brilliant.

A **question** asks for information or an opinion. It ends in a question mark.
What is penicillin?   Do you think germs are dangerous?

Question words are words that are useful for starting questions.
who   what   where   when   why   how

1 Read *Penicillin*. Write a **statement** to answer each **question**.

When was Alexander Fleming studying bacteria growth?
_____

What are bacteria?
_____

Who discovered penicillin?
_____

Where was Howard Florey from?
_____

How does penicillin work?
_____

2 Write a question for each answer.

_____   _____
_____   _____

> **Tip!** **Time words** and phrases help to sequence events.
> *then   later   since   the next day   on Saturday*

3 Find three phrases in *Penicillin* that show **time** or sequence.

_____   _____   _____

4 Use a **time word** from the box to complete each sentence.

| soon |
| now |
| afterwards |
| tomorrow |

The alarm clock will go off _____.

Shall we go _____?

I'll show you _____.

The expedition leaves _____.

5 Number these sentences from 1 to 5 in time order. Hint! Look at the **time words**.

☐ Today is Saturday and I have a soccer game.
☐ The next day my ankle was really sore.
☐ By Thursday it felt a lot better.
☐ Yesterday I could walk and run again.
☐ On Tuesday I had soccer practice and hurt my ankle.

 **Try it yourself!** Choose an event from the past that interests you. Write **questions** that you have about the event. Research the event and write a **recount** that tells the events in **time** order.

Reflection
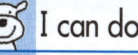 I can do this.
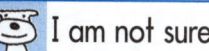 I am not sure.
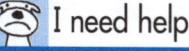 I need help.

Questions and statements; time words and phrases

Unit 10

Conjunctions, singular and plural nouns

Molly's Discovery

The sand squished between Oliver's toes. He was playing fetch with his dog, Molly, at the beach. It was a hot day and the beach was crowded so Oliver and Molly went further along the beach than they had ever ventured before, to the northern end, where nobody ever went. Oliver threw the ball but when Molly returned, the ball was not in her mouth. In her mouth was a small casket. Molly dropped it at Oliver's feet. Oliver bent down for a closer look. He picked it up, dusted off the sand and lifted the lid.

This imaginative text is the orientation of a *narrative*. It uses *singular* and *plural nouns* to introduce the characters and set the scene for the events.

Rule! Conjunctions are words that link ideas in a sentence.
and   so   but

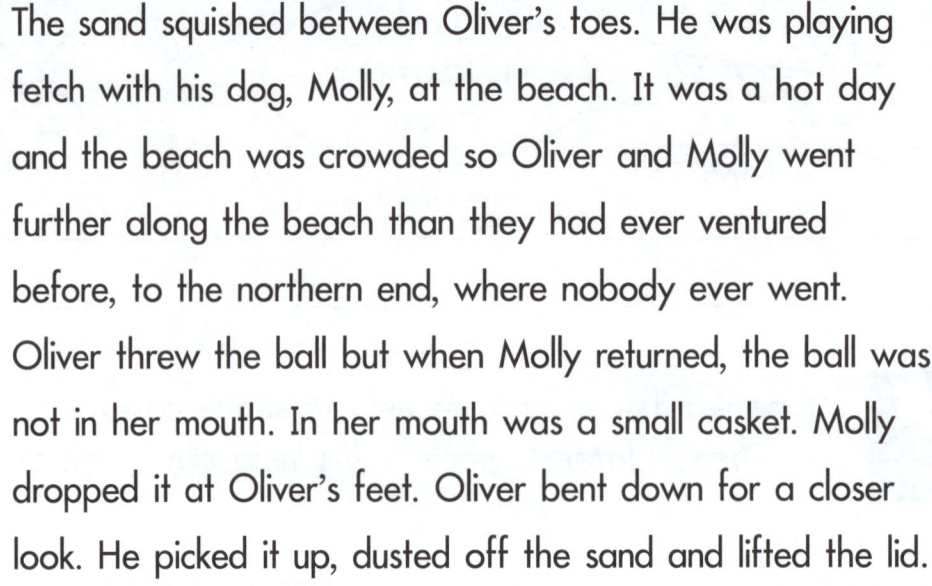

1 Read *Molly's Discovery*. Circle the **conjunctions**.

2 Complete each sentence with a **conjunction** from the box.

| because |
| therefore |
| so that |
| unless |

You won't get a turn _____ you give it back.

Give it back _____ you can have a turn.

You gave it back _____ you want a turn.

You gave it back _____ you can have a turn.

3 Use a **conjunction** to join each pair of sentences. Rewrite each pair as a single sentence.

| because |
| as well as |
| except |
| since |

I have missed Nick. Nick moved to Bathurst.
_____

I'm pleased you're here. Now we can test our device.
_____

It has buttons. It has lots of dials.
_____

Everyone can come. Benny can't come.
_____

Rule!

A **noun** can be **singular** or **plural**.
    singular: *apple*   plural: *apples*

A noun can be made **plural** by:
- adding –s or –es on the end   *dog* → *dogs*   *beach* → *beaches*
- changing the spelling in another way   *mouse* → *mice*   *person* → *people*

Some nouns don't change at all from singular to plural.   *fish*   *sheep*

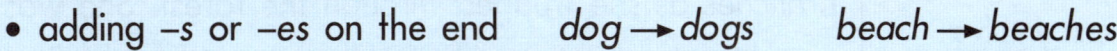

4 Write the **plural** of each **singular noun**.

dog _____   boy _____   girl _____

ball _____   beach _____   mouth _____

toe _____   lid _____   casket _____

5 Write the **singular** of each **plural noun**.

people _____   feet _____   men _____

women _____   leaves _____   lollies _____

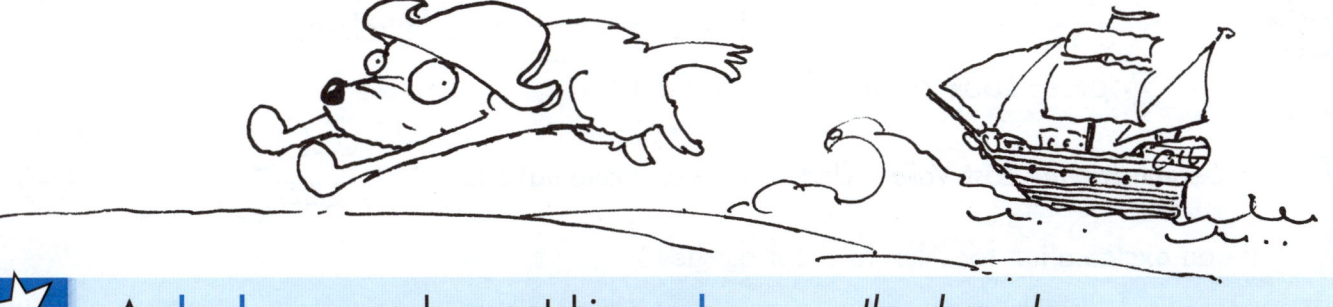

Rule!

A **plural noun** needs a matching **verb**.   the dogs play
A **singular noun** needs a matching **verb**.   the dog plays

6 Cross out the incorrect **verb** in each sentence.

The girl (run/runs) to her soccer coach.

The boys (swims/swim) very quickly.

The children (eat/eats) lunch at midday.

Try it yourself!

What will Oliver find in the casket? Create a storyboard. Label the storyboard and use **conjunctions** to link ideas. Finish the **narrative** or write a story of your own.

Reflection

I can do this.
I am not sure.
I need help.

Conjunctions (connectives); singular and plural nouns; subject/verb agreement

Unit 11

Exclamations, adverbs

This imaginative text is the orientation of a **narrative**. **Adverbs** tell how things happen. Use of **onomatopoeia** at the beginning appeals to the senses.

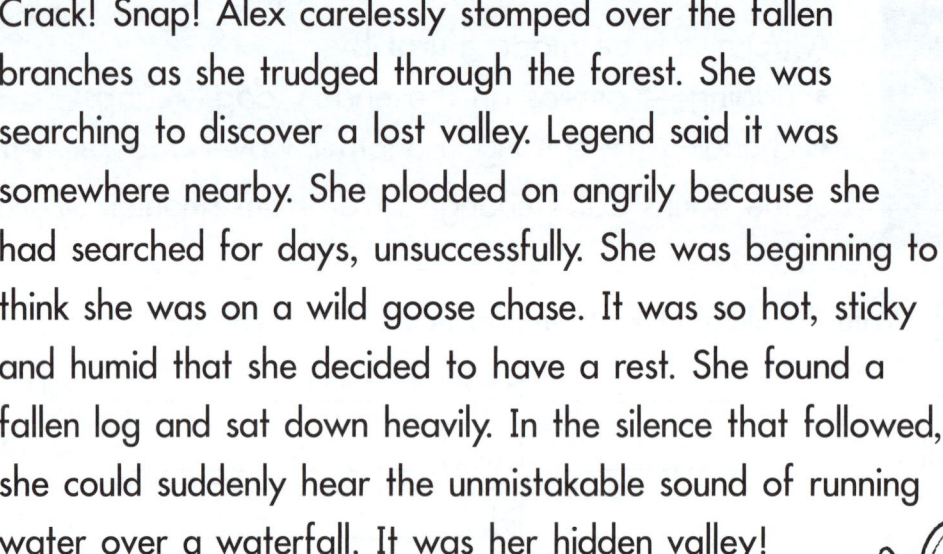

Search for the Lost Valley

Crack! Snap! Alex carelessly stomped over the fallen branches as she trudged through the forest. She was searching to discover a lost valley. Legend said it was somewhere nearby. She plodded on angrily because she had searched for days, unsuccessfully. She was beginning to think she was on a wild goose chase. It was so hot, sticky and humid that she decided to have a rest. She found a fallen log and sat down heavily. In the silence that followed, she could suddenly hear the unmistakable sound of running water over a waterfall. It was her hidden valley!

Rule! An **exclamation** is a sentence that shows strong emotion, or gives a warning or command. An **exclamation** ends in an exclamation mark.
  Stop!   Look at that!   I love it!

1 Read *Search for the Lost Valley*. Underline three **exclamations**.

2 Write an **exclamation** for Alex to shout as she:

stomped on a fallen branch _____

plodded angrily _____

heard the waterfall _____

3 Write an **exclamation** for each picture.

_____   _____

_____   _____

Rule! **Adverbs** are words that tell <u>how</u>, <u>when</u> or <u>where</u>. Some **adverbs** add meaning to **verbs** by telling <u>how</u>. Many **adverbs** end with the letters *–ly*.
quickly   suddenly   happily   busily   carefully

4 Write five **adverbs** ending in *–ly* from *Search for the Lost Valley*.

_____

5 Use an **adverb** from the box to complete each sentence.

| fiercely |
| wildly |
| crazily |
| carefully |

The child laughed _____.
The wind blew _____.
The child carried the puppy _____.
The lion growled _____.

6 Use each **adverb** in a sentence.

| quickly   noisily   happily   sadly |

_____
_____
_____
_____

Tip! **Onomatopoeia** is the name given to words that sound like the thing they represent. *bang   crash   pop*

7 Find two **onomatopoeia** words in *Search for the Lost Valley*. _____ _____

8 Write an **onomatopoeia** word for a sound made by each thing.
a dog _____   a cat _____
a snake _____   sausages frying in a pan _____

Try it yourself! Write a **narrative** of your own. Include **onomatopoeia** to represent sounds. Add **exclamations** to show when characters are angry, excited or surprised. Use **adverbs** to tell <u>how</u> actions happen.

Reflection
😊 I can do this.
😐 I am not sure.
☹ I need help.

Exclamations; adverbs to tell how; onomatopoeia

27

Unit 12 Revision

1 Circle the preposition in each row.

apple	monkey	eat	in
bed	beside	kiss	stop
umbrella	rain	under	mud
orange	wish	want	over

2 Complete each sentence with a preposition.

Sit _____ Johnny and Rashid.

Look _____ the chimney.

I ran _____ the path.

Put your socks _____ your shoes.

3 Write a prepositional phrase to complete each sentence.

I like to swim _____.

I wear a hat _____.

The mice jumped _____.

I keep my tools _____.

4 Write two adjectives to describe each noun.

_____ _____ chimpanzee

_____ _____ banana

_____ _____ gadget

5 Choose a relating verb from the box to complete each sentence.

| is | was | have | are |

Elephants _____ trunks.

Whales _____ mammals.

Igor _____ my friend.

I _____ on the telephone.

6 Cross out the incorrect personal pronoun in each sentence.

They will take me with (they/them) to the park.

(She/Her) is a great goalkeeper.

(It/He) is a good cook.

The CD is Billy's, give (it/them) back.

Nonna went skydiving with (him/he).

7 Write an exclamation that shows:

surprise _____

a warning _____

8 Imagine a famous person is coming to your school. Write a list of **questions** to ask him or her.

Name of famous person: _____

What _____

Where _____

How _____

When _____

Why _____

9 Use a **time word** or **phrase** to complete each sentence.

| tonight |
| this morning |
| tomorrow |
| soon |

I won't be able to sleep _____.

_____ is my birthday.

We made my birthday cake _____.

It will be cooked _____.

10 Use a **conjunction** from the box to join each pair of sentences. Write the new sentences.

| because   except |

I love playing netball. I am a good goal shooter.

_____

The dog can come inside. The dog cannot come inside when it has muddy feet.

_____

11 Write the **plural** of each **singular noun** so that there is more than one.

hat _____   table _____   child _____

12 Write the **singular** of each **plural noun** so that there is only one of each thing.

feet _____   toes _____   wishes _____

13 Use an **adverb** from the box to complete each sentence.

| happily |
| slowly |
| quickly |
| lazily |

The old cat yawned _____.

The children played _____.

The birthday cake was eaten _____.

The tortoise plodded _____ across the sand.

Unit 13

Evaluative words, quoted speech

Trampolines

"Dad," asked Henry, "Do you think the trampoline was a good invention?"

"I'd say that jumping on a trampoline is good exercise, as much fun as jumping on the bed but probably safer than jumping on the bed," Dad suggested. "What do you think?"

"I really like jumping on the bed but I'm not allowed," reminded Henry.

"You certainly are not allowed to jump on the bed. Jumping on the bed is dangerous with all the furniture nearby, so it's just as well the trampoline was invented," lectured Dad.

This text is a **discussion**. Each person makes persuasive statements that tell their point of view.

Rule! **Quoted speech** is the actual speech someone says. It is written inside **speech marks**.
"What do you think?" asked Dad.

1 Read *Trampolines*. Highlight the words that Dad says. Use a different colour to highlight the words that Henry says.

2 Work with a partner. One of you say Dad's speech. One of you say Henry's speech. Then add some extra **questions** and **statements** to their **discussion**.

3 Write what Henry would say next as **quoted speech**.

_____

4 Write what Dad would say next as **quoted speech**.

_____

5 Add **speech marks** to show which words are being said. The **speech marks** go outside the punctuation.

I want a turn! shouted Billy.   That's so funny, giggled Marie.

Dad whispered, Santa Claus might bring a trampoline.

Can I have a turn? begged Susan.

6 Write the saying verbs used in *Trampolines* for

how Dad speaks _____ _____

how Henry speaks _____ _____

7 Circle the saying verbs in the box.

| whispered yelled swam whined laughed asked peeped |

> **Rule!** **Evaluative words** tell us people's opinions and judgements about something.
> <u>delicious</u> food   <u>brave</u> explorer

8 Write down some evaluative words in *Trampolines* that tell you Dad's opinion.

about trampolines _____

about jumping on the bed _____

> **Rule!** **Apostrophes** can be used in shortened forms of words. They show that a letter or letters have been left out. The shortened forms are called **contractions**.
> she is → she's   I have → I've

9 Find three contractions in *Trampolines*.

_____   _____   _____

10 Write contractions for the words.

is not _____   can not _____

would have _____   should have _____

I will _____   you will _____

Try it yourself! Discuss your favourite game or sport with a partner. Record part of the **discussion**. Use **speech marks** to show what was said. Use **saying verbs** to tell how each person spoke.

Reflection
- I can do this.
- I am not sure.
- I need help.

Unit 14
Point of view, emotive words

This imaginative text is from a **narrative**. The two characters use **emotive words** to try to convince the other to do what they want.

The Thing Inside

"No Deni, I really don't want to go in there," argued Amy.

"Don't be a chicken. We might discover treasure, and it will be fun," Deni fumed.

"You've heard the stories about that house! What if they're true? Also, it's trespassing," Amy explained, with her arms folded in front of her.

"What if? What if? What if? Look, the fact is, there is absolutely no such thing as a ghost," Deni announced convincingly. "So, stay here or come with me but I'm going in."

Deni walked up the front steps of the derelict old house. The floorboards creaked and groaned at her every step. She stopped at the front door and turned back towards Amy.

"Well?" she asked, raising her eyebrows.

Tip! **Body language** and **tone of voice** are often used in arguments to reinforce a point of view. **Body language** includes gestures and facial expressions. **Tone of voice** means the sound of your voice.

1 Read *The Thing Inside*. Highlight the words that Deni says. Use a different colour to highlight what Amy says.

2 Work with a partner. One of you say Deni's speech. One of you say Amy's speech. Use **body language** and **tone of voice** to reinforce their points of view.

3 What **body language** does Amy use in *The Thing Inside*?

_____

What do you think her **body language** means?

_____

4 What **body language** does Deni use in *The Thing Inside*?

_____

What do you think her **body language** means?

_____

5 Write Amy's point of view and reasons. Write Deni's point of view and reasons.

Amy	Deni
_____	_____
_____	_____
_____	_____
_____	_____

> ⭐ **Tip!**
>
> **Emotive words** are words that appeal to the emotions. **Emotive words** are sometimes used to make arguments more persuasive.
>
> *It will be <u>fun</u>.*
>
> Other words can be used to make arguments more persuasive.
>
> no   yes   must   must not   do   don't   absolutely   definitely

6 Tick the sentence in each pair that makes a stronger argument.

I really love pizzas. ☐   I love pizzas. ☐

I want to go. ☐   I think I want to go. ☐

It's probably haunted. ☐   It's definitely haunted. ☐

It might not be yours. ☐   It is not yours. ☐

7 Who will win the argument in *The Thing Inside*? Deni or Amy? Write your reasons.

_____

_____

Try it yourself! Work with a partner. Choose a topic to **argue** about. Take opposite points of view. Express your points of view very strongly. Use **emotive words**, **tone of voice** and **body language**.

Reflection
- I can do this.
- I am not sure.
- I need help.

Point of view; modality; emotive words; body language

Unit 15

Commands, prepositional phrases

This **procedure** gives directions. It uses **commands** to tell what to do.

Where to Find the Hidden Treasure

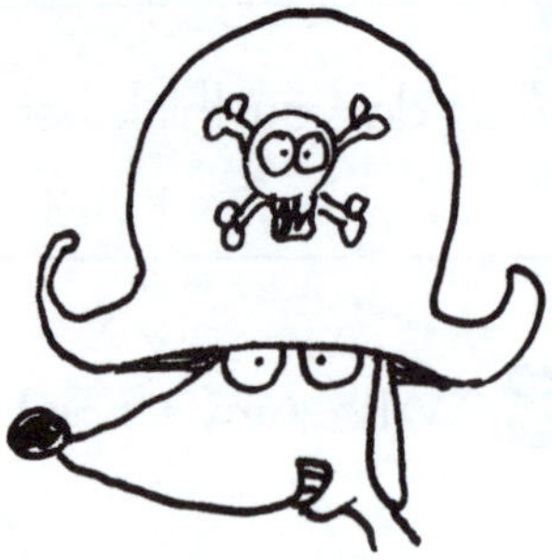

1. Start at the big oak tree in the backyard, facing the house.
2. Step sideways five paces to your left towards the dog's kennel.
3. Step backwards ten paces towards the fence.
4. Turn towards the water tank.
5. Slither on your stomach three body lengths towards the tank.
6. Dig down beneath your waist until you reach the treasure.

Rule! A **command** is a sentence that tells someone to do something. It often begins with a **verb**.

1 Read *Where to Find the Hidden Treasure*. Write the seven **doing verbs**.

_____

2 Replace each **doing verb** with another suitable **doing verb**. Use a thesaurus or dictionary for help.

start _____   step _____

slither _____   dig _____

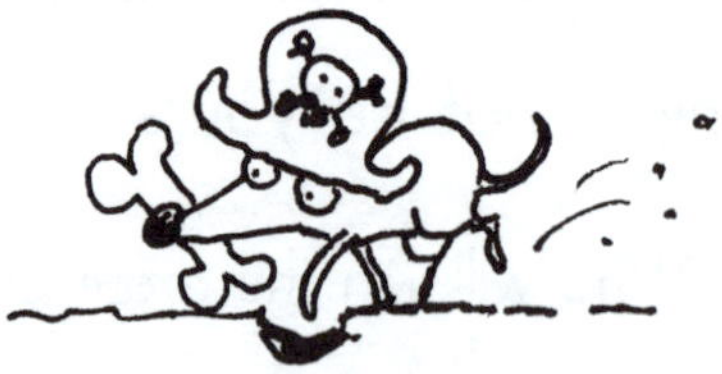

3 Tick to show whether each sentence is a **command**.

	Command	Not a command
Have you found the treasure yet?		
The treasure is buried in my yard.		
Use a shovel to dig in the ground.		
Have you seen the water tank?		
Share the treasure with your friends.		

Tip! Directions are written in a logical order. They are often set out in numbered steps.

4 Number these directions in order from 1 to 5.
- ☐ Walk out the door of your bedroom.
- ☐ Start at your bed.
- ☐ Go in and brush your teeth.
- ☐ Turn left and walk down the hall.
- ☐ Walk through the first doorway on the right side of the hall.

5 Write a set of directions to get from your bed to your bathroom. Use **doing verbs**.

1. _____
2. _____
3. _____
4. _____
5. _____

6 Circle the phrases that tell <u>where</u> in *Where to Find the Hidden Treasure*. Hint! They begin with these **prepositions**:
   at, in, to, towards, towards, towards, towards, beneath

Tip! Remember the rule on page 19.

7 Underline the **prepositional phrase** in the text that tells <u>how</u> to do something. Hint! It begins with *on*.

Rule! Some **adverbs** add meaning to verbs by telling <u>where</u>.
   up   nearby   here   there

8 Underline the **adverbs** that tell <u>where</u>.

Step sideways five paces.   Step backwards ten paces.

Dig down until you reach the treasure.

Try it yourself! Write a set of **directions** to reach a certain place or to discover buried treasure. Write the directions in logical order. Use **prepositional phrases** and **adverbs** to tell <u>where</u> and <u>how</u>. Ask a peer to help edit your work.

Reflection
- 👁 I can do this.
- 😐 I am not sure.
- ☹ I need help.

Commands; doing verbs; prepositional phrases and adverbs

Unit 16 — Emotive words, modality

This persuasive text is an advertisement. It uses **emotive words** to try to persuade people to buy a product.

Wiz Bang 3000 Kitchen Hand!

Have you ever needed a spare hand in the kitchen?
Do you often run out of time to chop your food?
Do you ever run out of time to cook your food?
Do you ever run out of time to clean up the mess and do the dishes?
Do you ever wonder if you will have enough time to eat your food?
We now have the answer for you:

The WIZ BANG 3000 KITCHEN HAND!

It chops, cooks, cleans and also feeds you your food.
Just ask for a meal from your WIZ BANG 3000 KITCHEN HAND and it will do everything.
But be quick, because THE WIZ BANG 3000 KITCHEN HAND has almost sold out.
So hurry and get this *amazing* invention today!

 Don't miss out! Buy now!

> ⭐ **Tip!** **Emotive words** are used in advertisements to persuade people to buy something.

1. Read *Wiz Bang 3000 Kitchen Hand*. Underline the **emotive words** that might convince a reader to buy one straight away.

2. *Wiz Bang 3000 Kitchen Hand* uses the **emotive words** 'Don't miss out'. How do you feel when you miss out on something that you really want?

3 Circle the words that could make the reader feel they need to hurry.

rush   hasten   slow down   dawdle   plod   act now   dally   delay   run   crawl

> **Rule!**
> Advertisements are very certain in the claims they make about products. Advertisements use words to show certainty or **high modality**.
> will   will not   must   must not   should   should not   definitely
>
> **Low modality** words are not used in advertisements.
> might   may   possibly

4 What does the advertisement claim that the Wiz Bang 3000 Kitchen Hand can do?

_____

_____

5 Tick the statements that show **high modality**.
- ☐ I will have a lunch order today.
- ☐ You might like to come.
- ☐ You must hug your teddy.
- ☐ I might have toast for breakfast.
- ☐ They will be late.

You must hug your teddy.

6 The first part of the advertisement asks the reader a series of questions. Talk with a partner. What is the function of the questions?

_____

_____

7 In *Wiz Bang 3000 Kitchen Hand* circle the **personal pronouns** that refer to the reader.

> **Tip!** Remember the rule on page 10.

8 Find the **pronouns** that refer to the Wiz Bang 3000 Kitchen Hand. Underline them in red.

9 Find the **personal pronoun** that refers to the makers of the Wiz Bang 3000 Kitchen Hand. Underline it in blue.

> **Try it yourself!**
> Write an **advertisement** for a household appliance. Use a real appliance such as a toaster or an electric toothbrush, or invent a new appliance. Use **high modality** and **emotive words** to convince people to buy your appliance.

Reflection
- 😊 I can do this.
- 😐 I am not sure.
- ☹ I need help.

Emotive words; modality (modal verbs, modal adverbs); personal pronouns

Unit 17
Articles, comparing adjectives

DISCOVERY: A New Species

It was the strangest and most peculiar thing I had ever seen: the way it hopped around on its hind legs; the way it appeared to balance on its huge tail; its beady little eyes; its tail and hindquarters too big for its body; its head too small. (I decided that the creature must have a very tiny brain.) I wondered if that quite frightening-looking tail was used as a weapon. It looked capable of doing some damage. However, the creature did not come closer and I gladly returned to the safety of the ship.

This informative text uses **noun groups** to **describe** an animal.

Rule!

An **article** is a word at the beginning of a noun group.
    the   a   an   <u>the</u> tail

Use 'a' before words that start with a consonant (<u>a</u> bird).
Use 'an' before words that start with a vowel (<u>an</u> emu).

1 Circle the correct **article** in each **sentence**.

We saw (a / an) creature.

It had (the / a / an) strong tail.

It had (the / a / an) amazingly small head.

(The / An / A) animal hopped away.

We returned to (the / a / an) ship.

2 Read *Discovery: A New Species*. Underline all the **noun groups**.

3 Write five **adjectives** from *Discovery: A New Species*.

Grammar Rules!

_____'s Writing Log

1 Think
What is your topic?
What is the purpose of the writing?
Who is the audience?
What type of text and text form will you use?

2 Draft
Gather your ideas.
Organise your ideas.
Have a go at writing.

3 Revise
Check your writing for meaning and ideas.
   Have you chosen the best words for your topic?
Does the structure match the type of text you chose?
Read your writing to a partner.
Read your writing to your teacher.
Ask for help to improve your writing.

4 Proofread
Polish your writing.
Check your grammar.
Check your spelling.
Check your punctuation.

5 Publish
Publish your writing.
Share your writing.
Reflect on your writing.

Create symbols for a rating scale. Then each time you finish a piece of writing, record it in the log.

My rating scale

Symbol   Meaning

☐   Help!

☐   A good start.

☐   I have the basics covered.

☐   I'm beyond the basics.

☐   Brilliant!

Do you need some ideas for other text forms to try? Look at the back page!

Date	Title	Type of text and text form	Audience
Write the date.	Write the title of your piece.	eg recount/ letter	Who were you writing for or to?

Grammar I used	My rating	Where to next?
List the main grammar features you used.	Record your rating.	What grammar could you try next? How could you improve your writing? Does your teacher have any comments?

I've tried these types of texts and text forms...

Narrative (imaginative)
- ☐ Story
- ☐ Comic
- ☐ Other _____

Recount
(imaginative or informative)
- ☐ Letter
- ☐ Newspaper article
- ☐ Other _____

Description
(imaginative or informative)
- ☐ Poem
- ☐ Wanted poster
- ☐ Letter
- ☐ Other _____

Response (persuasive)
- ☐ Diary
- ☐ Book review
- ☐ Poem
- ☐ Other _____

Exposition (persuasive)
(argues one side of an issue)
- ☐ Debate
- ☐ Speech
- ☐ TV advertisement
- ☐ Poster
- ☐ Other _____

Information report
(informative)
- ☐ Scientific report
- ☐ Website
- ☐ Other _____

Explanation (informative)
- ☐ Reference book
- ☐ Other _____

Procedure (informative)
- ☐ Cookbook
- ☐ Instruction manual
- ☐ Game rules
- ☐ Other _____

Discussion (persuasive)
(presents more than one side of an issue)
- ☐ Conversation
- ☐ TV interview
- ☐ Dialogue in a story
- ☐ Other _____

Rule!

Adjectives change form when used to compare things.
When comparing <u>two things</u> we often add –*er*.
   long → *longer*

When comparing <u>more than two things</u> we often add –*est*.
   long → *longer* → *longest*

4 Write the different forms for each **adjective** to compare things.

long	longer	longest
tall		
dark		
small		
great		

Rule!

Some **longer adjectives** need a different way to show **comparison**.
Adjectives with more than two syllables usually use:
- *more* for two things   The rose is <u>more beautiful</u> than the dandelion.
- *most* for more than two things   The rose is the <u>most beautiful</u> flower in the garden.

5 Complete each **sentence** with *more* or *most*.

The kangaroo is _____ ridiculous-looking than the giraffe.

The kangaroo is the _____ ridiculous-looking animal I've seen.

The tail was the _____ frightening part of the animal.

The tail was _____ frightening than the teeth.

6 Write the **comparing** forms of these **adjectives**. Hint! You'll find them in *Discovery: A New Species*.

strange _____   peculiar _____

Try it yourself!

Write a **description** of an animal. Use **noun groups** with **articles** and adjectives to build up your description. Be careful to use the right form when using **adjectives** to compare.

Reflection
- I can do this.
- I am not sure.
- I need help.

Unit 18 Revision

1 Add **speech marks** around the **quoted speech**.

Take me with you! screamed Louie.

I think that's a good idea, replied Pop.

I would like to go, too, suggested Rhami.

Marty sniggered, Good.

2 What does Dad say? Use **speech marks**.

What does Mum say? Use **speech marks**.

_____

_____

_____

_____

3 Write a **contraction** for each word or word group. Hint! Remember to use an **apostrophe**.

I am _____   cannot _____

I have _____   could have _____

do not _____   is not _____

4 Which sentences express the strongest opinion? Tick one box in each row.

I am very pleased. ☐   I am pleased. ☐

I might go. ☐   I will go. ☐

I think I lost my ball. ☐   I lost my ball. ☐

Dad might be home soon. ☐   Dad will be home soon. ☐

5 Circle the **doing verb** in each row.

science	scientist	invention	explode
read	computer	keyboard	teacher
submarine	shark	jump	frog
deer	rabbit	run	robot

6 Number the directions in logical order from 1 to 4.

☐ Turn on your computer.
☐ Open your file.
☐ Sit at your desk.
☐ Log in your name.

7 Complete each sentence with a **prepositional phrase** that tells <u>where</u>.

Run _____ .

Jump _____ .

Reach _____ .

8

> Try Jitto. You might like it.

> Buy Jetto. It tastes great and is good for you.

Which product would you buy? Give two reasons for your choice.

_____

9 Complete the table with **adjectives** that compare.

tall	taller	tallest
loud		
smart		
kind		

10 Write the correct form of the **adjective** in brackets.

One clown was _____ (funny) than the other.

The clown in the red hat was the _____ (funny).

My laboratory was _____ (tidy) than my assistant's.

My laboratory is the _____ (tidy) laboratory in the building.

11 Write a strong argument to respond to this.
"You have to do my homework. I don't have time," said Sis.

_____

Revision

Unit 19 — Ownership

> This imaginative text is a **poem**. It uses **idiom** and **simile** to build up descriptions.

Voyagers

Wind's howl
waves' rage
ship's sails strain.
Like a cork
we're tossed
thrown
taken where
winds demand
waves control.
Through uncharted seas
fearful –
hoping not to find
Davy Jones's locker.

Tip! An **idiom** is an expression that means something different from the usual meaning of the words.
raining cats and dogs

1 Read *Voyagers*. Write the **idiom** that means the bottom of the ocean.

_____

2 Why do the sailors say they hope not to find Davy Jones's locker?

_____

3 Draw a line to link each **idiom** with its meaning.

fit as a fiddle	something worthwhile
shake a leg	die
nothing to sneeze at	very healthy
crook as Rookwood	stranded
kick the bucket	hurry up
high and dry	very sick

> **Rule!**
> An **apostrophe** can show ownership. An apostrophe with a **noun** shows that something belongs to that noun.
> singular noun → add 's   *Shelly's treasure*
> plural noun ending in s → add '   *the pirates' code*
> plural noun not ending in s → add 's *the children's parrot*

4 Circle the four words in *Voyagers* that use an **apostrophe** to show ownership.

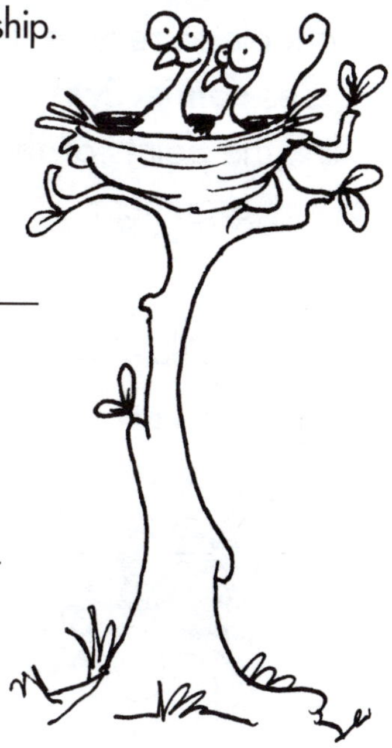

5 Use an **apostrophe** to show ownership with these **singular nouns**.

Molly owns the map _____

Oliver owns the compass _____

The rays of the sun _____

6 Use an **apostrophe** to show ownership with these **plural nouns**.

The twins own the chest _____

Sailors own the yachts _____

Birds own the nests _____

> **Tip!**
> A **simile** is a figure of speech. Something is spoken of as being <u>like</u> something else. The words *like* or *as* are used.
>   as quick as a fox   like a tiger

7 Draw a line to complete each **simile**.

slept like	a bone
as blind as	a log
the ship tossed like	a bat
stubborn as	a cork
dry as	a mule

Try it yourself! Interview teachers and family members. Ask them to suggest **idioms** and **similes**. Write a poem that uses one or more of their suggestions. Or, create a poster that illustrates one or more.

Reflection
- I can do this.
- I am not sure.
- I need help.

Apostrophe for possession in singular and plural nouns; simile; idiom

Unit 20

Fact and opinion

This persuasive text presents an **exposition** that tries to convince people to recycle. It uses **connectives** to link the points of the argument.

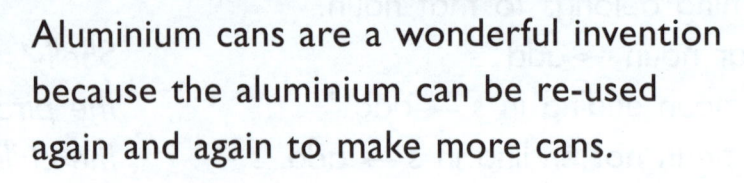

EVERYONE SHOULD RECYCLE

Aluminium cans are a wonderful invention because the aluminium can be re-used again and again to make more cans.

Today I would like to talk to you about recycling aluminium cans.

Firstly, I think that this is one great way to help the planet.

Secondly, it is easy and simple for anyone to do at home.

Finally, recycling aluminium cans saves you money: it is cheaper to recycle aluminium than make new aluminium and so recycling helps reduce packaging costs.

In summary, you should all do your bit to save the planet.

So, get active now and collect and recycle those cans!

Rule!

Connectives are words that link ideas through a text.
Connectives can be **conjunctions**.
    so   and   because
Connectives can also be other **words and phrases**.
    meanwhile   in addition   on the other hand

---

1 Read *Everyone Should Recycle*. Circle the **connectives**. Try to find five.

2 Number the sentences from 1 to 5 to show the sequence. Hint! The **connectives** will help you.

☐ So, choose sandwiches for lunch today.

☐ To begin with, sandwiches are healthy.

☐ Finally, sandwiches can easily be packed for school lunches.

☐ I think sandwiches are good for lunch.

☐ In addition, sandwiches are economical.

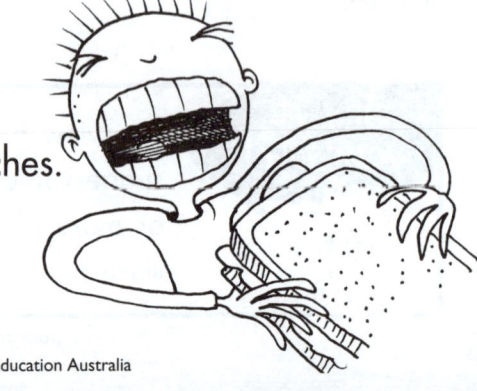

3 Use the connectives from the box to complete the paragraph.

| in addition | finally | while | secondly | firstly | and |

I believe that television is unhealthy. _____ it encourages people to sit around _____ not get any exercise. _____ people tend to eat more _____ they watch television. _____ the shows that are on television are very boring and do not stimulate the brain. _____ television stops families from having conversations.

Rule!

Language can express a **fact**. Factual statements are true.
The writer's or speaker's opinion is not obvious in a factual statement.
Most plastic is recyclable.

Language can express an **opinion**.
Plastic is a wonderful product.   Plastic is a dreadful product.

4 Draw lines to show if each noun group conveys a fact or opinion.

a black horse

the wattle tree in Nan's yard

a beautiful horse

the lazy dog

| Fact |

| Opinion |

Pop's poodle

the doddery old man

a bottlenose dolphin

annoying children

5 *Everyone Should Recycle* ends with a call to action. Write it here.

_____

Try it yourself! Write an **exposition** about something. Use **connectives** to link your ideas logically. End it with a call to action. Ask a peer to help edit your work. Rehearse your speech before presenting it to the class.

Reflection
I can do this.
I am not sure.
I need help.

Connectives; fact and opinion

45

Unit 21

Quoted speech

This imaginative text is a comic strip **narrative**. It uses speech balloons to show what the character is saying.

PROFESSOR SNODGRASS FAILS AGAIN

MEANWHILE, BACK AT THE LAB...

I'M GOING TO INVENT A CURE FOR STINKY FEET – OR, IN SCIENTIFIC TERMS, 'curus maximus stinkolata footitis'.

OOPS!

...BACK TO THE DRAWING BOARD.

Tip! In comic strips, **quoted speech** is shown in speech balloons. Speech marks are not needed.

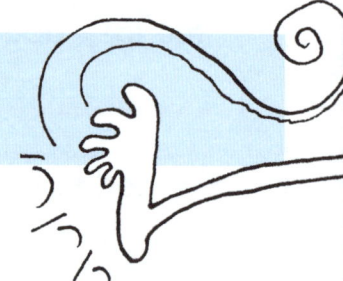

1 Read *Professor Snodgrass Fails Again*. Write what the Professor says on the lines below. Use complete sentences with **speech marks** and **saying verbs**.

_____

_____

_____

2 What would you say to Professor Snodgrass if you met him? Write your speech using **speech marks**.

_____

_____

_____

46   Grammar Rules! Student Book 3 (ISBN 9781420236590) © Tanya Gibb/Macmillan Education Australia

3 Write speech inside each speech balloon.

4 Read out loud the made-up term 'curus maximus stinkolata footitis'. Have a guess what each word could mean.

Tip! Cartoons and comic strips often use **stereotypes**. A stereotype is a caricature or an exaggeration. The image of Professor Snodgrass is a **stereotype**, not a true-to-life image of a professor.

5 Draw a line to connect each description to either <u>real-life scientist</u> or <u>stereotype comic strip scientist</u>.

- works in a laboratory or in the field
- male only
- may or may not wear glasses or contact lenses
- works in a laboratory only
- male or female
- wears crooked, broken glasses
- dresses professionally
- real-life scientist
- stereotype comic-strip scientist
- does crazy experiments and always causes explosions
- nutty and mad
- works safely
- wears daggy, nerdy clothes
- intelligent

Try it yourself! Create a comic strip of your own to tell a narrative. Base your comic strip on a character that you can **stereotype**. Use speech balloons for the **quoted speech**.

Reflection
- I can do this.
- I am not sure.
- I need help.

Quoted speech; stereotypes

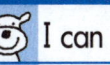

Unit 22
Reported speech, emotive words

This newspaper article **recounts** events that have happened. It uses **emotive words** to make events seem more interesting.

Daily News 7 August 2016

DINOSAUR FOUND AT LOCAL SCHOOL

Students and teachers at Sunny Side Public School were stunned yesterday when they unearthed a set of very large bones. The principal, Julie Chan, was assisting the environment club to extend their vegetable garden, when the bones were discovered. The bones were promptly sent to The University of Queensland and have since been confirmed to be dinosaur bones. Principal Chan said that the school community is very excited to have uncovered these incredible pieces of history.

Tip! News items sometimes use **emotive words** to sensationalise the writing. This creates interest.

1 Read *Dinosaur Found at Local School*. If you just read the headline, what would you think happened at the school?

_____

2 What would be a more accurate but less sensational headline?

_____

3 Which headline do you prefer, and why?

SCHOOL CHILDREN DIG UP DINOSAUR
SCHOOL FINDS DINOSAUR IN VEGIE PATCH
CHILDREN FIND DINOSAUR IN VEGIE PATCH
DINOSAUR FOUND IN CABBAGE PATCH

_____

Rule! **Reported speech** is speech that is not quoted directly. It does not need speech marks.
Principal Chan said she hoped more bones would be found.

4 Underline the sentence in *Dinosaur Found at Local School* that includes Principal Chan's **reported speech**.

5 Rewrite the **quoted speech** as **reported speech**.

Principal Chan said, "I'd like to thank UQ for its help."

_____

Angeline Frolie, a parent, said, "My children were too excited to sleep."

_____

"At first we didn't realise what we'd found," said teacher José Ramon.

_____

6 Work with a partner. One of you take on the role of a student at Sunny Side Public School. One of you take on the role of a newspaper reporter. Role-play an interview about the events in *Dinosaur Found at Local School*.
Now write up the interview as **reported speech**.

_____
_____
_____
_____
_____
_____
_____

Rule! Nouns can be **abstract**. *peace hatred*
Nouns can also be **concrete**. *chair horse*

7 Find and circle the **abstract noun** 'history' in *Dinosaur Found at Local School*. Underline three **concrete nouns**.

Try it yourself! Write a newspaper article that **recounts** something exciting happening at your school. Use **emotive language** to make the events sound exciting. Use **reported speech** to report what people say. Don't forget to write an attention-grabbing headline.

Reflection
- I can do this.
- I am not sure.
- I need help.

Unit 23
Tense, time words

The Jacket

Every year Ella's family went camping in the mountains. One night, after taking her little sister to their parents' tent, Ella noticed something colourful stuck in the tree branches above the campsite. It was too dark to see properly so she decided to wait until morning to have a better look. The next morning, as soon as she woke, Ella climbed the tree to see what was hidden in the branches. It was a high climb but eventually she reached the section of the tree that held the object. She discovered that it was a very small jacket, only big enough for a very tiny person, and there was something in the pocket.

This imaginative text is the orientation for a **narrative**. **Time words** and phrases help to sequence events.

Rule!
Verbs can show when an action happened. This is called the **tense**.
- **past tense** — she went
- **present tense** — she goes   she is going
- **future tense** — she will go

Time words and **phrases** also help tell when events happened.
yesterday   next   on Sunday

1 Read *The Jacket*. Underline four **time words** or **phrases**.

2 Verbs for the **past** often end in *–ed*. Circle five **past tense verbs** in *The Jacket* that end in *–ed*.

3 Tick a column to show the **tense** of each sentence.

	Past	Present	Future
I am hungry.			
I chased the cat.			
I will go to the park.			
You are standing in the way.			
You stepped on my toes.			

4 Complete the table.

Past	Present	Future
I jumped.	I am jumping.	I will jump.
I ate.		
	I am skipping.	
I played.		
I wrote.		
		I will help.

5 Add some other **past tense verbs** to replace *got* in this paragraph.

Ella (got) _____ down from the tree. She (got) _____ into her tent. She (got) _____ her sister to hold the jacket. She (got) _____ her torch and shined it at the jacket for a closer look.

6 Complete each sentence. Notice that each sentence starts with a **time word** or **phrase**.

As soon as _____

Eventually, _____

Now, _____

Finally, _____

7 Write the words in a **time sequence** for one day.

| before lunch | after dinner | during breakfast | at bedtime |

_____

Try it yourself! Write a **narrative** of your own. Write it in the **past tense**. Use **time words** and **phrases** to help show the sequence of events. Ask a peer to proofread and help edit your work.

Reflection
- I can do this.
- I am not sure.
- I need help.

Unit 24 Revision

1 Use an **apostrophe** to show ownership.

The dog belongs to Jude. It is <u>Jude's dog</u>.

The keys belong to Dad. They are _____.

The paw belongs to the cat. It is the _____.

The children own the skateboards. They are the _____.

The teachers own the cars. They are the _____.

2 Number the sentences from 1 to 5 to show the sequence. Hint! The **connectives** will help you.

☐ Therefore, I recommend soccer to everyone.
☐ Firstly, it gives you a lot of exercise.
☐ My third point is that it teaches you how to be part of a team.
☐ I think soccer is a great sport.
☐ Secondly, it teaches you lots of skills.

3 Write two **facts** and two **opinions** about your class.

Fact	Opinion
_____	_____
_____	_____
_____	_____
_____	_____

4 Add **speech marks** to show **quoted speech**.

Nana said, Your dad was fast as lightning when he was your age.

Dad said, Nan's memory is a shot duck.   What's a shot duck? I asked.

Something that is kaput, replied Dad.   Well, what's kaput? I asked.

Guess, said Dad.

5 Imagine that your school principal won the lottery and decided to take the whole school on a holiday to Fiji. Write a newspaper headline about it. Use **emotive words**.

_____

6 Change the **quoted speech** to **reported speech**.

The principal said, "I'm so happy to give the children a wonderful holiday".

_____

Katy Chung from Year 6 said, "I've always wanted to go to Fiji".

_____

"At first, we didn't believe him," said teacher Nadia Vonstag.

_____

7 Tick a column to show the tense of each sentence.

	Past	Present	Future
I am tired.			
I fed the hippos.			
Will we go to the park?			
You are blocking the doorway.			
You squashed the banana.			
We might go to the movies on Saturday.			

8 Cross out the incorrect **verb**.

I (go/went) to the shop yesterday.

I (buyed/will buy) a milkshake later.

Mary (played/plays) cricket last Saturday.

Rami (rid/rode) his bike to school this morning.

9 Number these sentences from 1 to 4 in time order.

☐ After school, we had gymnastics.

☐ Before lunch, we marked our homework.

☐ After lunch, we had art.

☐ Before school, I went to the library.

Revision

Unit 25 — Modality, connectives

THE BEST NEW INVENTION

A number of amazing inventions have been entered in the Best New Invention Competition.

Many people thought the Heli Cooler Hat should win because it keeps people cool on a hot day. The 40-centimetre blades are attached to the top of a sunhat. When the 'on' switch is pressed the blades whirl around like a fan.

Other people like the Santa Claus Detector because it sets off a silent alarm the second Santa Claus falls down the chimney.

Every child will want a Santa Claus Detector, I agree. However, my vote goes to the Heli Cooler Hat because I think it will be useful every day and it is also great for keeping people sun safe.

> This persuasive text is a **discussion** that summarises points of view. It uses **connectives** to link opinions with reasons.

1 Read *The Best New Invention*. Underline the **noun group** at the beginning of each paragraph.

Tip! Remember the rule on page 13.

2 Draw a line to link each paragraph in *The Best New Invention* with its function.

Paragraph 1	Present an opinion and give reasons.
Paragraph 2	Make a final recommendation or judgement.
Paragraph 3	Present a different opinion and give reasons.
Paragraph 4	Introduce the topic.

Rule! **Connectives** can link an <u>opinion</u> with a <u>reason</u>.

because   therefore   so   however   since   unless   in case   otherwise

3 Circle three **connectives** in *The Best New Invention* that link an opinion with a reason.

4 Choose a **connective** from the box to link each opinion to its reason.

| since | because | otherwise | so | unless |

I like apples better than oranges _____ they are sweeter.

I think you should take an apple _____ you prefer apples to oranges.

You don't like apples _____ take an orange in your lunch box.

I don't like apples _____ they are cooked

You should eat them before they go bad _____ they'll be wasted.

> **Tip!** In some situations, **high modality** words are not appropriate. In a discussion, for example, these high modality statements sound argumentative.
> *You must agree with me. I am definitely right.*
> A **low modality** statement is less argumentative.
> *Perhaps we could think about this. You might find I am right.*

5 Read *The Best New Invention*. Which words show **low modality**?

_____

6 Draw a line to link each comment to the person most likely to say it.

I see what you mean but I'm not sure I agree.

You are absolutely wrong.

I understand what you're saying.

That's a good point but I can't agree.

Maybe you have a point.

That is a stupid suggestion.

Your opinion is ridiculous.

You can't be serious.

The Arguer

The Discusser

Try it yourself! Discuss your favourite gadget or invention with a partner. Use **low modality** words such as *I think, possibly, perhaps, what do you think*? Record the opinions presented and the reasons for them in a written **discussion**. Use the same structure as in *The Best New Invention*.

Reflection
- I can do this.
- I am not sure.
- I need help.

Noun groups; modality; connectives

Unit 26

Lexical chains, adjectives

This imaginative text is a two-stanza **poem**. It uses **adjectives** to **describe**.

Breakfast Inventions

Toaster
Kitchen hero
Working every day
Making hot, crispy breakfasts
Champion.

Cereal
Wholegrain flakes
Breakfast of champions
Crunchy, nutty, fruity, delicious breakfast.

Tip! A **metaphor** is a figure of speech. Something is spoken of as if it _is_ something else.
   My cat is the queen of the house.

1 Read *Breakfast Inventions*. What is the **metaphor** in the first stanza?

_____

Rule! **Lexical chains** are made up of words that link a particular content strand in a text. A lexical chain about machines could be:
   computer → robot → calculator → gadget

2 In *Breakfast Inventions*, circle the words that make up the **lexical chain** related to the toaster. Underline the words that make up the **lexical chain** related to cereal.

3 Create a **lexical chain** of words for your favourite breakfast.

_____

Rule! **Descriptive adjectives** can describe colour, shape, size or quality.
pink   oval   huge   fuzzy

4 Write the **descriptive adjectives** from *Breakfast Inventions*.

toast _____ _____

cereal _____ _____ _____ _____

5 Draw a line to match each **descriptive adjective** with a **noun**.

Descriptive adjectives	Nouns
fluffy	cactus
blue	box
prickly	monster
square	possum
hideous	iceblock

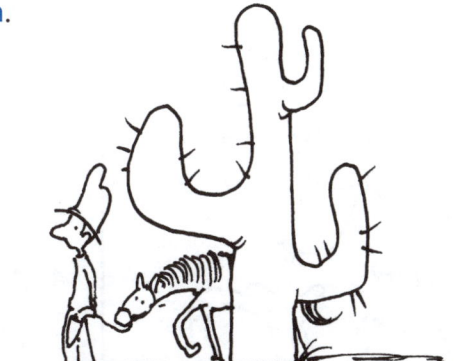

6 Decide whether each **adjective** describes colour, shape, size or quality. Then write each **adjective** under the correct heading.

hungry   enormous   red   filthy   gigantic   slow
white   circular   round   tiny   square   green

Colour	Shape	Size	Quality
___	___	___	___
___	___	___	___
___	___	___	___

7 Complete the paragraph with **descriptive adjectives**.

We had a _____ dinner at the restaurant for Dad's birthday. The chow mein was _____. The satay chicken was _____. The restaurant also makes _____ fried rice. Dad said he had a _____ night.

Try it yourself! Write a **poem** that **describes** a place, a thing or a person. Use **descriptive adjectives**.

Reflection
I can do this.
I am not sure.
I need help.

Unit 27

Number adjectives, commands

Wart, Fester and Carbuncle Remover

INGREDIENTS

- 1 cup milk
- 100 g grated candle wax
- 1 tablespoon very hot chilli powder
- 10 mL nail polish remover
- 2 cups vinegar

METHOD

1. Mix all ingredients to a paste.
2. Apply a thin film of paste over affected areas.
3. Bandage affected areas.
4. Avoid water for four weeks. (This means no baths or showers.)

What is a carbuncle, anyway?

This **procedure** is a recipe. It uses **number adjectives** in the **noun groups**.

Rule!

Number adjectives tell you about the <u>quantity</u> or <u>order</u> of a noun.

   one   two   three   5   10   first   second   last

Some **number adjectives** are precise.   five   7   second

Some **number adjectives** are vague.   many   some   few

1 Read *Wart, Fester and Carbuncle Remover*. Underline the **number adjectives**.

Are they precise or vague? _____

Tip!

Number adjectives in recipes need to be precise.

2 Complete each sentence with a word or words from the box. Make sure each sentence makes sense.

| enough |
| a pinch |
| 1 cup |
| 1 litre |
| 2 tablespoons |

Add _____ of salt.

Add _____ water to make a smooth paste.

Add _____ of sugar.

Stir in _____ of milk.

Mix with _____ of chocolate powder.

3 Underline the **number adjectives**.

The third runner is my friend.

A few friends are coming.

I won second prize for my invention.

I have three cats.

Many schools organise excursions to the museum.

A hundred people went to the concert.

> **Tip!** The method of a recipe is a series of **commands**. Most commands start with a **doing verb**.
> Sometimes commands start with an **adverb** that tells <u>how</u> to do something.

4 Write the **doing verbs** in *Wart, Fester and Carbuncle Remover*.

_____ _____ _____ _____

5 Use an **adverb** from the box to start each **command**.

| carefully | briskly | gently | totally |

1. _____ mix all ingredients to a paste.
2. _____ apply a thin film of paste over affected areas.
3. _____ bandage affected areas.
4. _____ avoid water for four weeks.

6 Circle the word in each line that could be used in a recipe.

giggle	rope	mix	hat
busy	desk	school	fry
stir	jump	television	nose
giraffe	bake	nail	poison

Try it yourself! Create a **recipe** to cure a real sickness or a made-up sickness such as school fever or breatho stinko o'lot'o.
Use **number adjectives** for the amounts of each ingredient.
Use **doing verbs** or **adverbs** to start the **commands**.

Reflection
- I can do this.
- I am not sure.
- I need help.

Number adjectives (quantifiers); commands; doing verbs; adverbs to tell how

Unit 28
Connectives

This informative text is an **explanation**. It uses time and cause **connectives** to explain how something works.

How Does the Alarm Bed Work?

1. An alarm clock, attached to the head of the bed, rings when it is time to get up.

2. Once it rings the sleeper has five minutes to get out of bed because that alarm starts a five-minute timer in the mattress springs.

3. If the pressure on the mattress springs has not changed when the five minutes are up (in other words, if the sleeper is still in the bed) then a latch at the head of the bed is released. This causes the mattress and bed base to catapult forward.

4. This, in turn, causes the sleeper to be ejected from the bed.

Tip! **Explanations** often include flow charts and diagrams to help make them easier to understand.

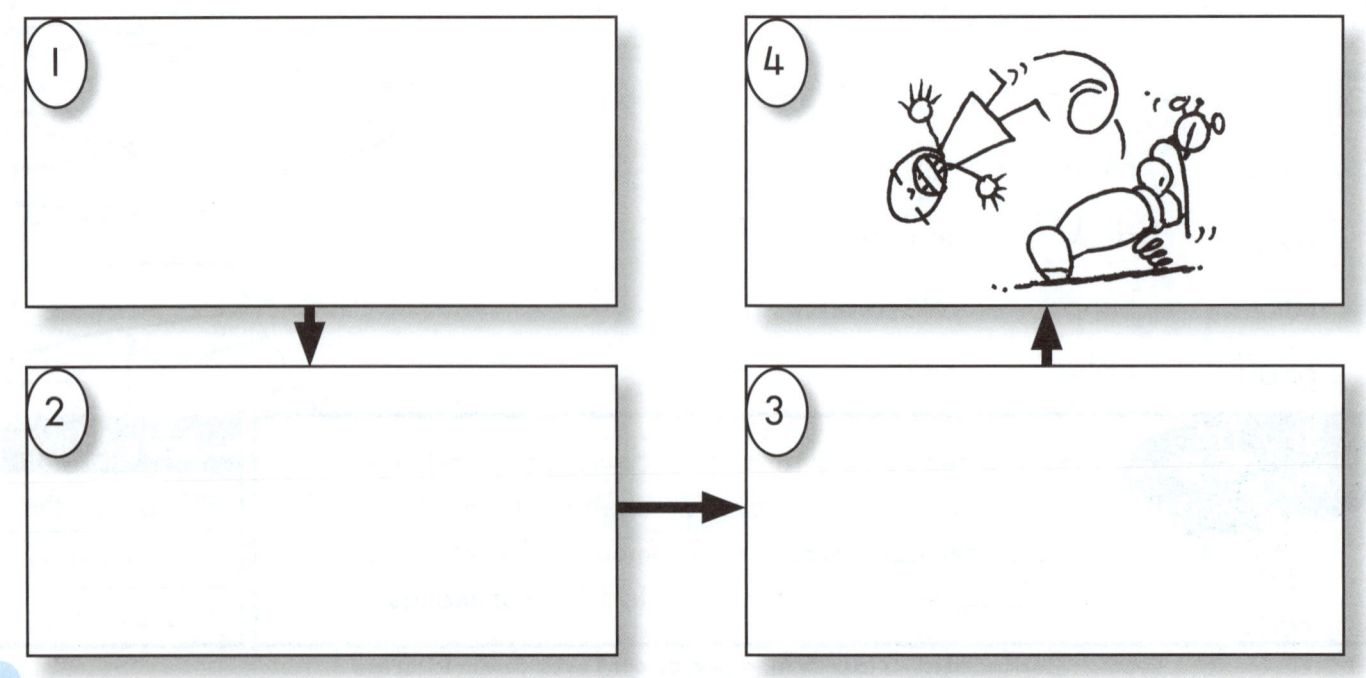

1 Read *How Does the Alarm Bed Work?* Draw steps 1, 2 and 3 in the flow chart. Add labels.

Rule!

Some **connectives** show a time sequence.
    then   *next*   *until*

Some **connectives** show that one thing causes another thing.
    so   *because*   *in turn*

2 In *How Does the Alarm Bed Work?* underline all the words that show <u>time</u> sequence.

3 In *How Does the Alarm Bed Work?* circle all the words that show that one thing <u>causes</u> another thing.

4 Write the **doing verb** for each step in the process.

a. The alarm clock _____.
b. The alarm clock _____ a timer.
c. The timer _____.
d. The latch _____.
e. The mattress and bed base _____.
f. The sleeper is _____.

5 Choose three **technical words** used in *How Does the Alarm Bed Work?* Use a dictionary and write their definitions.

_____
_____
_____

6 Write a list of things you would need to construct the alarm bed. These things will be **nouns**.

_____
_____

7 Use **evaluative words** to write your opinion of the invention. Is it useful? Will it work? Will people buy it and use it?

_____
_____
_____

Tip! Remember the rule on page 31.

Try it yourself! Create an invention of your own. You may like to work with a partner to brainstorm ideas. Then write an **explanation** to tell how the invention works. Use **connectives** to show time and to show cause and effect.

Reflection
- I can do this.
- I am not sure.
- I need help.

Connectives; doing verbs; nouns; technical language; evaluative language

Unit 29 — Classifying adjectives

How to Use the Drolley (or Dog Trolley)

1. If you have a number of dogs to walk at the same time, attach each dog's lead to a hook on the Drolley. Then push the Drolley to walk the dogs.

2. The Drolley has brakes if any dog is pulling too hard.

3. If any dog does its business, use the Drolley's plastic-lined suction hose to suck up the business. Then treat it with environmentally safe chemicals. Once treated, use the dog business to fertilise your garden.

4. Rewards such as dog treats and drinking bowls can be stored in the Drolley's tray.

This **procedure** provides instructions. It uses **classifying adjectives** in the noun groups.

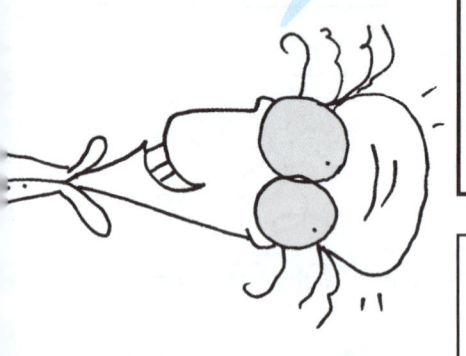

1 Read *How to Use the Drolley*. Draw a diagram to go with the instructions. Add labels.

Rule!
Classifying adjectives tell the group that a **noun** belongs to.
<u>drinking</u> bowl   <u>suction</u> hose   <u>football</u> match
To test if an adjective is a **classifying adjective**, try to add the word *very* in front of it. It won't make sense.
a very <u>drinking</u> bowl

2 Circle all the **noun groups** in *How to Use the Drolley*.

What kind of hose is used in the Drolley? _____

What kind of lead is attached to the Drolley hooks? _____

What kind of chemicals are used? _____

What kind of treats are stored in the tray? _____

What kind of bowls are stored in the tray? _____

What kind of trolley is the Drolley? _____

3 Use a **classifying adjective** from the box to classify each **noun**.

| rain | oak | fruit | Siamese | chocolate |
| gold | hand | marsupial | money | football |

_____ tree   _____ cat   _____ fish
_____ cloud   _____ box   _____ cake
_____ boot   _____ juice   _____ bag
_____ mouse

4 Use **evaluative words** to write your opinion of the Drolley. Is it useful? Will it work? Will people buy it and use it?

Tip! Remember the rule on page 31.

_____
_____
_____

5 Complete each sentence.

The Drolley works best when _____

The Drolley topples over if _____

The Drolley's wheels freeze up when _____

The treated dog business is released when _____

Try it yourself! Write a **procedure** (instructions) for using a piece of equipment. Or, invent something and then write instructions to describe its features and how to use it.

Reflection
- I can do this.
- I am not sure.
- I need help.

Noun groups; classifying adjectives; evaluative language

Unit 30 Revision

1 Complete each sentence with a **connective** from the box.

| so | since | unless | in case | otherwise |

_____ we can't have cake, let's have ice-cream.

Take your raincoat _____ it starts to rain.

Start your homework straight away. _____ you won't finish before dinner.

_____ you start now you won't be finished before dinner.

Get your homework finished _____ you can watch some television.

2 Decide whether each **adjective** describes colour, shape, size or quality. Then write each **adjective** under the correct heading.

| gigantic | grey | minuscule | smooth | cool | rectangular | narrow | black |

Add two extra words of your own to each column.

Colour	Shape	Size	Quality
_____	_____	_____	_____
_____	_____	_____	_____
_____	_____	_____	_____
_____	_____	_____	_____

3 Replace *good* with different **descriptive adjectives**.

We saw a (good) _____ show on television the other night. It was about otters. They looked (good) _____. They had a (good) _____ home off the coast of Alaska. Mum said they had a (good) _____ life there.

4 Complete each sentence by explaining how each thing works. Use **connectives** to show that one thing causes another thing.

Bells work _____

_____

Dog leashes work _____

_____

5 Complete each sentence with a **number adjective** from the box.

some
many
2
1
2

Buy _____ litres of milk, please.

Buy _____ batteries, please.

_____ ducks swam on the lake.

Stir in _____ cups of flour.

Swallow _____ teaspoon of medicine.

6 Underline the **number adjectives**.

Our school won first prize in the music festival.

The debating team won a few medals.

Most schools organise some excursions for their students.

Thousands of people went to the football match.

7 Choose an **adverb** to begin each command.

carefully
gently
clearly
slowly

_____ describe your invention.

_____ stir the mixture while it heats.

_____ collect the eggs.

_____ pat the puppies.

8 Choose one **descriptive adjective** and one **classifying adjective** for each noun.

Descriptive adjectives: exciting   healthy   cute   fresh   ferocious

Classifying adjectives: boxer   male   football   orange   breakfast

_____   _____ game

_____   _____ tiger

_____   _____ puppy

_____   _____ juice

_____   _____ cereal

Unit 31

Collective nouns, pronouns

My Home

We belong to the land.
The land does not belong to us.
When White Man came
He did not know this.
He wanted to own everything.
He caused problems.
He took over the land
for his houses and farms.
He cleared it
and put up fences.
He took all the fish from the rivers
and polluted them with his waste.
He hunted and killed the kangaroos
and other wild creatures.
He said,
"We own this land.
There is no place for You."
And so…
My tribe vanished.

This imaginative text is a **poem**. It gives a **point of view**.

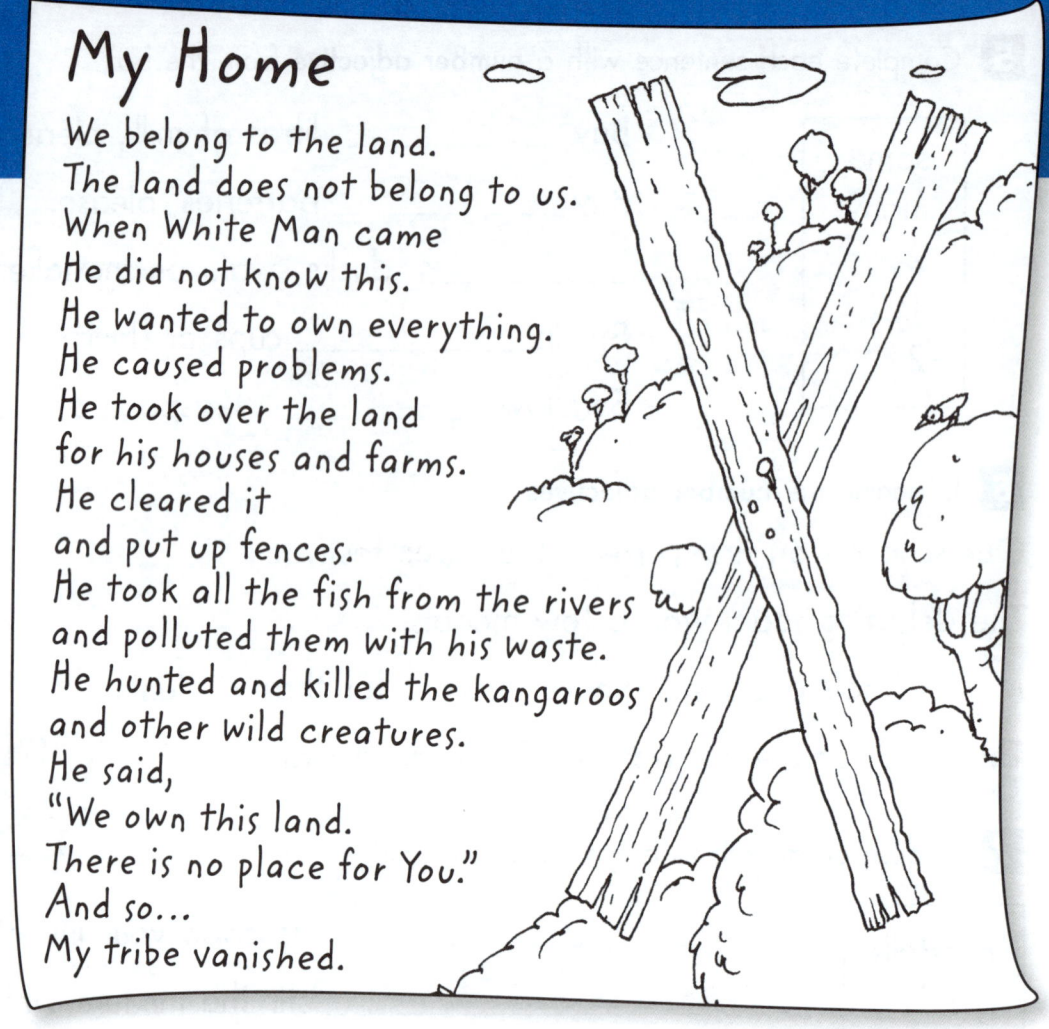

1 Read *My Home*. Who do you think is telling the story in the poem?

_____

2 Find three **evaluative words** in *My Home*.

_____ _____ _____ _____

3 What would the White Man say to the poet in response to *My Home*?

_____

_____

> **Rule!**
> **Personal pronouns** replace **nouns**.
> They can refer to the person or people speaking. *I me us we*
> They can refer to the person or people being spoken to. *you*
> They can refer to people, animals, things and places being spoken about.
> *it they them*

4 Underline the personal pronouns in *My Home*.

Rule!

Collective nouns are names for groups of things. **Collective nouns** are **singular** even though they refer to a number of things in their group because there is <u>one</u> group.
 bunch   bouquet   flock   gang

5 Look up *tribe* in the dictionary. Write its definition. *Tribe* is a **collective noun**.

_____

6 Draw a line to match each **collective noun** to the people, animals or things it refers to.

flock   horses
library   seagulls
pod   books
pack   whales
herd   flowers
bunch   wolves

7 Use a **collective noun** from the box to complete each **noun group**.

clutch	team
litter	herd
flock	school

a _____ of kittens   a _____ of eggs

a _____ of players   a _____ of cows

a _____ of ducks   a _____ of fish

Try it yourself!

Think about people in history who have had different **points of view**. Write a **poem** that shows the differences.

Reflection
- I can do this.
- I am not sure.
- I need help.

Unit 32
Types of sentences

This persuasive text is a **discussion**. It shows different **points of view**. It includes a variety of **sentence types**.

Trying to Negotiate

"Pack up all your equipment, now," requested Mum.

"Why can't we work on our project a bit longer?" whined Billy.

"We need to set the table for dinner. Your experiment will have to wait until tomorrow," insisted Mum.

"But Mum," added Aggie, "we just got everything organised. Can we just have another half an hour?"

"No! There's no time. I think it's a great project but it can wait. Finish it tomorrow," declared Mum.

1. Read *Trying to Negotiate*. Highlight what Billy says in blue. Highlight what Mum says in red. Choose a different colour and highlight what Aggie says.

2. Circle the **saying verbs** in *Trying to Negotiate*.

3. Write the **exclamation** from *Trying to Negotiate*.
   _____

Tip! Remember the rules on page 22, 26 and 34.

4. Choose one **command** from *Trying to Negotiate*. Write it on the line.
   _____

5. Write the two **questions** from *Trying to Negotiate*.
   _____
   _____

6. Choose one **statement** from *Trying to Negotiate*. Write it on the line.

7 Write a **sentence** on each line. Use correct punctuation marks.

Statement _____

Question _____

Command _____

Exclamation _____

8 Rewrite each sentence with correct punctuation.

wow yelled lucy _____

where is my hat questioned karl _____

i love lasagne stated fema _____

stop shouted the coach _____

Rule! **Synonyms** are words that are similar in meaning.
huge → enormous → big

9 Write three **synonyms** that could be used instead of *whined* in *Trying to Negotiate*.

_____

10 Write three **synonyms** that could be used instead of *declared* in *Trying to Negotiate*.

_____

11 Sometimes the word *said* is used too often in texts. This can make the text sound boring. What other words could you use in your writing instead of *said*? Start a list of **synonyms** here.

_____

_____

Try it yourself! Write a **discussion** between two or three people. Show that they have different opinions. Use punctuation marks and include statements, questions, commands and exclamations.

Reflection
- I can do this.
- I am not sure.
- I need help.

Statements, questions and commands; exclamations; quoted speech; synonyms

Unit 33 — Lexical chains, evaluative words

*This diary entry is a **response**. **Lexical chains** link content words.*

Dear Diary,

My brother, the little scallywag, has ruined everything. I made an invention to lure mice out of hiding and capture them without chopping off their heads. But my meddling pest of a relative, the one whose name is Ben, has broken the trap and set the mice free in the garden. Mum is screaming blue murder. Monster brother is laughing his head off. I am in big trouble. That five-year-old is going to get it from me.

Until tomorrow, Katy.

1 Read *Dear Diary*. Circle the words that make a **lexical chain** for the brother.

2 Circle the words that make a **lexical chain** for mice.

Tip! Remember the rule on page 56.

Mice are my favourite pets. These furry little rodents are likeable. Their cute little whiskery faces make me smile. I love having their little paws crawl up my arm.

3 Circle the words that make a **lexical chain** for food.

When I go shopping I need to buy carrots, pumpkin, potatoes, apples, bananas, milk, cling wrap, batteries and bread.

4 In *Dear Diary*, what opinion does Katy have about her brother?

_____

5 What is Mum's opinion about the events?

6 What is Ben's opinion about the events?

_____

7 If Ben accepts that he acted wrongly, what will he say to Katy? Use **evaluative words**. Remember to use **speech marks**.

_____
_____

> **Tip!** Remember the rule on page 31.

8 If Ben thinks what he did is OK, what will he say to Katy? Use **evaluative words**. Remember to use **speech marks**.

_____
_____

9 What might Mum say? Write her **quoted speech**. Use **evaluative words**.

To Katy _____

To Ben _____

10 Write a **lexical chain** for _mouse_. Include names for a mouse and mouse actions.

_____
_____

11 Circle two words in each row that are **synonyms**.

lime	green	apple	grape
predict	weather	rain	forecast
like	hate	soaked	wet
enjoyed	liked	party	hope
laugh	talk	chuckle	tickle

> **Tip!** Remember the rule on page 69.

Try it yourself! Write a **response** as a diary entry that tells your thoughts and feelings about something. Use **evaluative words**. Use **synonyms** to make your writing more interesting.

Reflection
- I can do this.
- I am not sure.
- I need help.

Lexical chains; quoted speech; speech marks; synonyms; evaluative language

Unit 34

Personal pronouns

The Invention of Money

This informative text is an **information report**. It uses **personal pronouns** to refer to people or things.

It is thought that the Greeks invented the first money over two and a half thousand years ago. They made coins out of a mixture of gold and silver. Before the invention of money people traded items of value. For example, a farmer might trade a cow for two pigs. Other items that people traded were rice, tobacco, animal furs, whale teeth and gold. Gold was a popular trading item but it was too heavy to carry around, so people wrote promises on pieces of paper saying they would pay in gold. The first true paper money was probably invented in China.

1 Read *The Invention of Money*. Circle the words that make up the **lexical chain** related to money and trade.

Rule! **Personal pronouns** stand for the people or things spoken about.
  they   them

2 Find a **personal pronoun** in *The Invention of Money*. _____

Who or what does the **pronoun** refer to? _____

3 Write five **noun groups** used in *The Invention of Money*.

_____

_____

Tip! Remember the rule on page 66.

4 Write two **proper nouns** for people or countries used in *The Invention of Money*.

_____

5 Find two technical words in *The Invention of Money*. Look them up in a dictionary and write their definitions.

_____

_____

Rule! **Commas** are used to separate items in a list of nouns. The word *and* is usually used instead of a comma between the last two items.
rice, tobacco, animal furs, whale teeth and gold

6 Write lists. Use **commas** between each item and the word *and* between the last two items.

girls' names _____, _____, _____ and _____

boys' names _____

names for mice _____

items you could trade _____

_____

Rule! **Homophones** are words that sound the same but are spelled differently and mean different things.
flour and *flower*

7 Find a **homophone** for *two* and *to* in *The Invention of Money*. _____

8 Choose the correct **homophone** from the box to complete each sentence. Hint! A dictionary will help you.

| weather | flour | by | sail | their |

The _____ of the boat fluttered in the breeze.

The _____ was very mild.

_____ sailboat was very slow.

_____ the time the wind picked up we had to go home.

I ran out of _____ to make the cake.

Try it yourself! Do some research on a topic of your choice. Write an **information report**. Use **personal pronouns** to stand for the people or things you are writing about. Be careful not to give your opinions. Only write the facts.

Reflection
- I can do this.
- I am not sure.
- I need help.

Personal pronouns; noun groups; commas in noun lists; homophones

Unit 35 Revision

1 Write five **collective nouns**.

_____

2 Write a **question** to ask a teacher.

_____

3 Write an **exclamation** you might hear at school.

_____

4 Write a **command** you might hear at home.

_____

5 Underline the **personal pronouns**.

I will discover the cure.

She is a famous inventor.

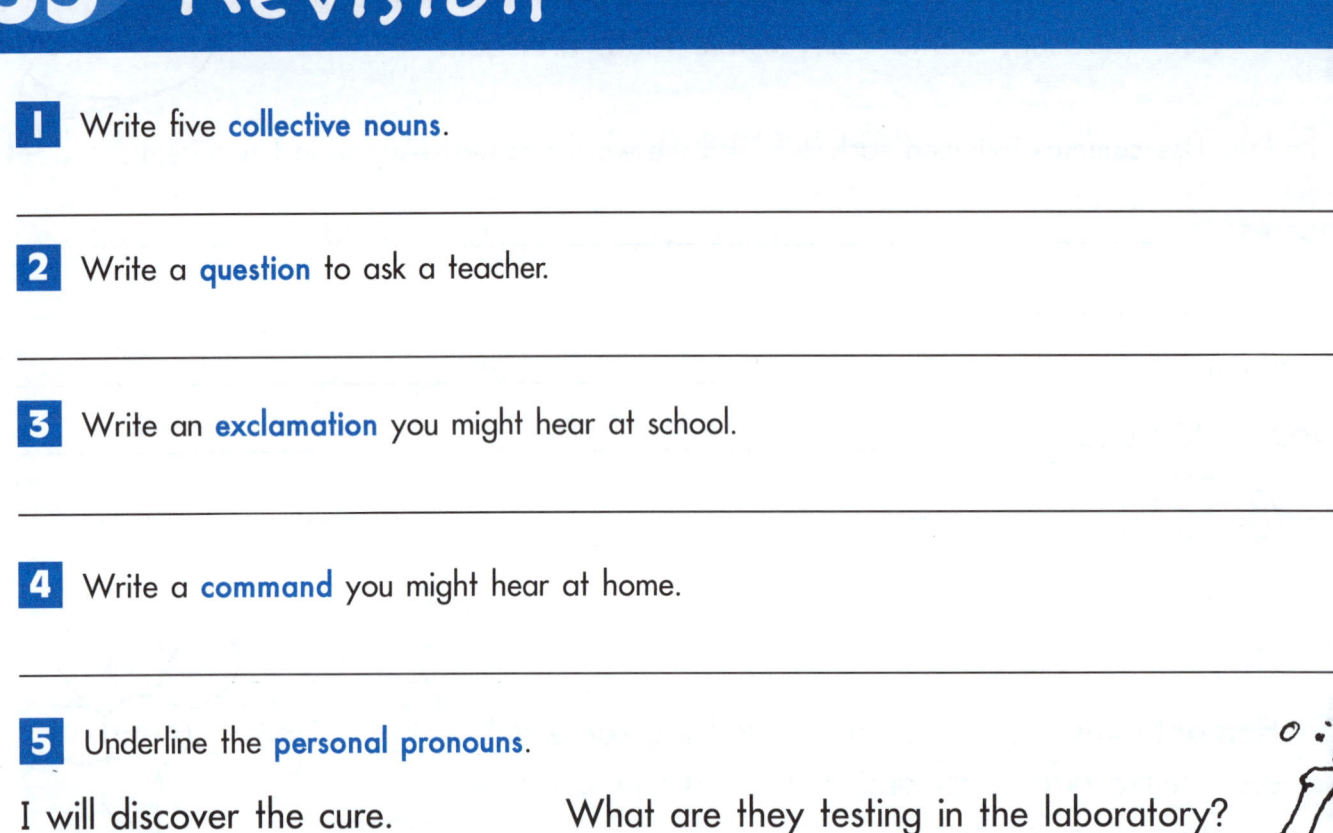

What are they testing in the laboratory?

Give the test results to him.

6 Write three **verbs** on each line.

Doing verbs _____

Thinking and feeling verbs _____

Relating verbs _____

Saying verbs _____

7 Write three **synonyms** for _big_.

_____   _____   _____

8 Underline the **evaluative words**.

My cousin is greedy.

That's a funny movie.

I think the gold is too heavy.

The red car is cool.

9 Add **commas** to this sentence.

We will need a hammer some nails a piece of paper a pen and our thinking caps!

10 Add punctuation to these sentences.

oh gasped Ralph

does anyone have the football asked Jordan

come here commanded the teacher

we need to finish our group project today reminded Sunita

11 Write a *lexical chain* of words for activities in your classroom.

_____

_____

12 Find the grammar terms in the findaword grid.

| adjective | verb | phrase | preposition | connective | conjunction |
| sentence | punctuation | noun | pronoun | adverb | tense |

p	u	n	c	t	u	a	t	i	o	n	x
r	a	v	e	r	b	n	t	e	n	s	e
e	d	a	x	c	x	t	m	b	b	x	e
p	j	d	w	e	r	o	o	i	o	c	v
o	e	v	u	y	t	n	f	v	n	o	i
s	c	e	i	i	p	y	r	e	z	m	t
i	t	r	f	o	p	m	t	e	i	m	c
t	i	b	g	h	j	n	r	t	u	a	e
i	v	d	c	n	e	s	a	r	h	p	n
o	e	x	u	s	p	r	o	n	o	u	n
n	e	o	c	l	a	u	s	e	o	p	o
s	n	o	i	t	c	n	u	j	n	o	c

GRAMMAR RULES

Look at the page number in the star to find more information about the rule.

adjective .... a word that describes a **noun** ⭐13

        classifying adjective ⭐62

        comparative and superlative adjectives ⭐39

        descriptive adjective ⭐57

        number adjective ⭐58

adverb .... a word that adds meaning to a **verb**, **adjective** or another **adverb**. Adverbs can tell how, when or where.

        adding meaning to **verbs** *by telling* <u>how</u> ⭐27

        adding meaning to **verbs** *by telling* <u>where</u> ⭐35

article .... a word at the beginning of a noun group

        a an the ⭐38

clause .... a group of words including a verb ⭐11

command .... a sentence that tells someone to do something ⭐34

conjunction .... a word that links ideas in a **sentence**. Conjunctions are **connectives**. ⭐24

connective .... a word or words that link ideas through a text ⭐44

        linking an opinion with a reason ⭐54

        showing time sequence ⭐61

        showing one thing causes another thing ⭐61

evaluative word ... a word that tells us someone's opinion and judgement about something ⭐31

exclamation ...... a sentence that shows strong emotion, or gives a warning or command. An exclamation ends in an exclamation mark. ⭐26

lexical chain ..... a chain of words that link a particular content strand in a text ⭐56

modality .... the degree of certainty the speaker or writer has about something. **High modality** is certain; **low modality** is uncertain. ⭐37